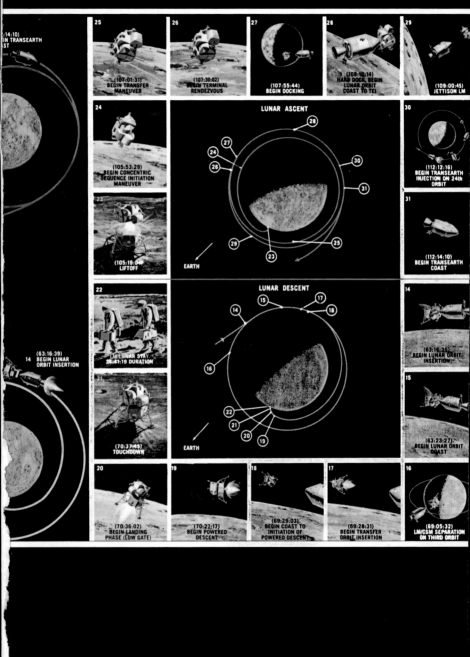

(114:10)
IN TRANSEARTH
AST

25 (107:01:31)
BEGIN TRANSFER
MANEUVER

26 (107:30:02)
BEGIN TERMINAL
RENDEZVOUS

27 (107:55:44)
BEGIN DOCKING

28 (108:18:14)
HARD DOCK, BEGIN
LUNAR ORBIT
COAST TO TEI

29 (109:00:45)
JETTISON LM

24 (105:53:29)
BEGIN CONCENTRIC
SEQUENCE INITIATION
MANEUVER

23 (105:19:04)
LIFTOFF

LUNAR ASCENT

28 27 24 26 30 31 29 23 25

EARTH

30 (112:12:16)
BEGIN TRANSEARTH
INJECTION ON 24th
ORBIT

31 (112:14:10)
BEGIN TRANSEARTH
COAST

22 LM LUNAR STAY
33:41:19 DURATION

(63:16:39)
14 BEGIN LUNAR
ORBIT INSERTION

21 (70:37:45)
TOUCHDOWN

LUNAR DESCENT

15 17 18 14 16 22 21 20 19

EARTH

14 (63:16:39)
BEGIN LUNAR ORBIT
INSERTION

15 (63:23:27)
BEGIN LUNAR ORBIT
COAST

20 (70:36:02)
BEGIN LANDING
PHASE (LOW GATE)

19 (70:27:17)
BEGIN POWERED
DESCENT

18 (69:29:03)
BEGIN COAST TO
INITIATION OF
POWERED DESCENT

17 (69:28:31)
BEGIN TRANSFER
ORBIT INSERTION

16 (69:05:32)
LM/CSM SEPARATION
ON THIRD ORBIT

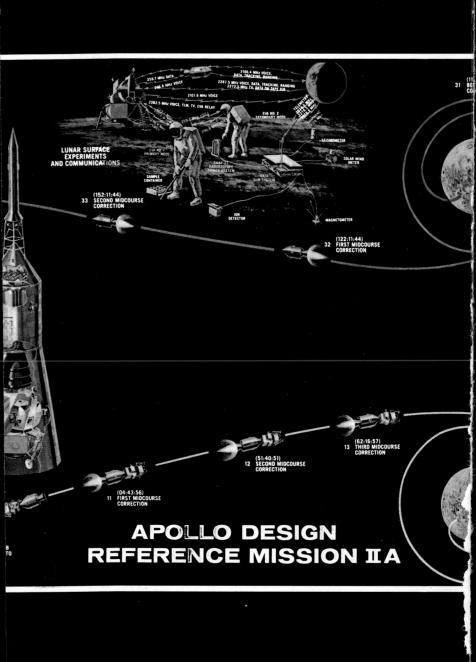

2106.4 MHz VOICE, DATA, TRACKING, RANGING

259.7 DATA

296.8 MHz VOICE

2287.5 MHz VOICE, DATA, TRACKING, RANGING
2272.5 MHz TV, DATA ON TAPE DUB

2101.8 MHz VOICE

2282.5 MHz VOICE, TLM, TV, EVA RELAY

(11
31 BE
CO

**LUNAR SURFACE
EXPERIMENTS
AND COMMUNICATIONS**

EVA NO. 1
PRIMARY MODE

EVA NO. 2
SECONDARY MODE

SEISMOMETER

SOLAR WIND
METER

SAMPLE
CONTAINER

SNAP-27
RADIOISOTOPE
POWER SYSTEM

DATA
SUB SYSTEM

(152:11:44)
33 SECOND MIDCOURSE
CORRECTION

ION
DETECTOR

MAGNETOMETER

(122:11:44)
32 FIRST MIDCOURSE
CORRECTION

(62:16:57)
13 THIRD MIDCOURSE
CORRECTION

(51:40:51)
12 SECOND MIDCOURSE
CORRECTION

(04:43:56)
11 FIRST MIDCOURSE
CORRECTION

B
TO

APOLLO DESIGN
REFERENCE MISSION II A

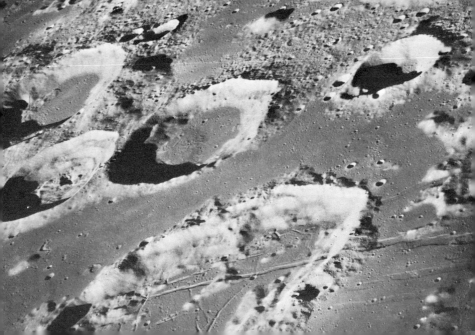

earth, moon and beyond

BOB W. PARROTT

WORD BOOKS, PUBLISHERS
WACO, TEXAS—LONDON, ENGLAND

TO
My wife, Doris
One of Truth's best teachers

PREFACE

In my book, "A Man Talks With God," I caught glimpses
of Him in what some would call the smallest events in life.
God came on strong to me through a children's dog show; a
red-velvet cake; rolling East Texas hills, and other almost in-
significant situations.

In the writing of that book and later writings, I found myself geared so keenly to God-in-every-little-thing that I almost
overlooked God in one of the biggest events of our day—
the trip to the moon! When Dr. Wilmot Hess, head of NASA's
science applications division and a member of my congregation, said, "It would be interesting to read your observations
of the Apollo project," my search for truth suddenly expanded
to include the age in which we live—the space age.

As I now think about the moon trip, the voice of truth
shakes my soul as strongly as the blasting lift-off roar of Saturn
V shook the very ground I stood on.

In this book I am not trying to belabor an issue, to debate
the academic pros and cons about the put-a-man-on-the-moon-
in-this-decade emphasis, or to discuss political priorities. Within the pages of this book I am extending my search for truth

to include situations involving manned lunar exploration—and beyond.

In this book are revelations of truth as that truth came to me through personal experiences with persons involved with NASA's Manned Spacecraft Center here at Houston, Texas. Of the many hundreds of extraordinary space pictures, this book holds some of the most thought-provoking ones. Drawing on inspiration furnished by these pictures, I have a part of this book labeled: "Truth Through Space Pictures." Then there were times within the Manned Spacecraft Center environs that I was inspired to write about my personal experiences. Those times make up another part of this book. And then quite naturally at home, at the office, on the freeways, in my plane flying crosscountry, I mused philosophically and theologically about our travels to the moon, to Mars and beyond. Those moments were times of soul-searching. And I believe there is truth to what is written in these personal meditations.

This book from its inception (before its inception because it took many meetings with NASA's science heads before this book idea was formed) has been a search for truth. That search has come in varying types of situations which invariably make for different kinds of musings.

You never have truth, capture it, or control it. Truth hits you when you least expect it. In this book when the truth hit me, I wrote about it.

At all times in my writing, I am being theological because I believe God to be the God of truth as revealed in Jesus of Nazareth. It is this faith approach which makes the book open-ended. I am not trying to prove anything. You don't prove truth. That remains constant no matter what anybody says. All we can do is point to the truth. These events in this book about which I write are not preconceived. They are happenings.

Let's look at it another way: truth is a positive power that relates itself to any situation. There is an element of truth in even the seamy side of life. But if we see only the seamy side of the situation, we have not seen the truth. In every Peyton Place affair, in every battlefield, in every evil situation there is right there in the middle of it a positive spirit of truth wrestling with the negative forces that demoralize, degenerate, and kill. While this aspect may not be caught by some script writers of "realism," truth is nonetheless there trying to forgive, redeem, and save.

If truth is the positive power working in the evil situations, it should not be too difficult to accept that truth is the positive power working in what looks like positive human situations. Truth wills to make something good out of the worst man does; that spirit wills to make something good out of man's best efforts.

We are putting our best foot forward (or brains!) here at the Manned Spacecraft Center of NASA. Truth is never an "aginner." Truth wants something good to happen here.

What's really happening here? It's easy to see and sometimes hard to forget the tragic deaths of those brave men in this program. Evil seemed to have the upper hand in those days. And it's anybody's guess if or when such may occur again.

But we must not forget—truth is trying to speak to us, trying to redeem, trying always to save for the good of all. It is within the framework of this conviction that I attempt this search for truth in this biggest scientific and technological event in mankind's entire history—manned lunar landing.

There can be no formal conclusion to this book. At the moment this manuscript is printed I am sure that a new truth will appear on the horizon of my mind, but it will be too late for inclusion in the book. But that's the way truth works, and that truth I accept.

I hope that the reading of this book becomes for you an event through which God reveals truth to you. And that you will continue to be open to Him in this space age.

My thanks to Dr. Wilmot Hess for suggesting this book idea, for opening many doors at the Manned Spacecraft Center, and for his generous introduction to "Earth, Moon, and Beyond." Without his support this book could not have been.

And to Mr. Paul Penrod whose counsel helped me chart my course.

And to Mr. Herbert Tiedemann, NASA geologist, whose expert research supplied precise captions for the book's space pictures that NASA so graciously provided.

And to Dr. P. R. Bell, the evangelist for space science! His enthusiasm for life and for discovery of what our Creator is doing brings life to the party. And I use the word "party" realistically. Because every serious discussion I've had with the science community at NASA turns into a joyful experience when "P.R." arrives.

And to Astronaut Tom Stafford whose editorial criticisms, along with those of Dr. Hess, Dr. Bell, and the wives of both scientists, have given this book correct expressions of scientific and technological truths.

And to all others, the astronauts, their wives, engineers, technicians, and scientists who graciously cooperated with this writing venture by sharing their thoughts and feelings with you.

Where possible each musing was proofread by the individuals involved. Thus in a very real sense the scientific material in this book has the best documentation. It comes from "the horse's mouth," the primary source being the people themselves.

At no time did any of these men tell me what to write; their only question was: "How can we help you?"

And to my patient, devoted secretary, Mrs. Jan Havis, who shared my enthusiasm for this project from the beginning.

My final word of gratitude must be to my wife, Doris, and daughter, Deborah, who, second to God, heard these musings on the moon. Their objective, critical remarks whittled away the manuscript's crudeness and helped mold it into what it is.

CONTENTS

INTRODUCTION

The churches are an active and integral part of the community about the Manned Spacecraft Center near Houston, Texas. Rev. Bob Parrott, Minister of the Seabrook Methodist Church, locally known as the "Astronaut's Church," is in a position to know intimately and appreciate the goals and efforts of the people in the Manned Spacecraft Program. His congregation includes astronauts, senior engineers, flight surgeons, Ph.D.'s, secretaries, plus shrimp fishermen and oilmen. It is a very moving experience to sing the hymn "Lord, Guard and Guide the Men Who Fly" in Bob's church when one of the congregation is flying a spacecraft several hundred miles in space.

P. R. Bell and I encouraged Rev. Bob Parrott to write this book. We are members of his church, we like his sermons, and we like Bob. P. R. Bell and I are both scientists working with NASA and we tend to view the space program from the inside. We find it exciting and consuming in terms of science and engineering and spacecraft. In this book Bob includes a different look at our business, in terms of men, of God, of philosophy, and the search for truth.

Bob has ridden the simulators with astronauts, has visited the Lunar Receiving Laboratory where the moon rocks will reside, and has watched an Apollo launch from Cape Kennedy. He also flies his own airplane. He tells of these experiences and the people involved in them, and then "muses" on his observations in terms of daily living as seen through the eyes of a thoughtful Christian. Recent space photographs of the earth and moon also bring forth "musings." An expanding view of the earth and heavens brings to him a realization of an expanding view of God.

Bob Parrott has great enthusiasm in the search for truth, whether it be in discovering God, or discovering the answers to scientific questions, or in personal relationships. He brings these three domains together in *Earth, Moon, and Beyond.* Many of his queries are left for history to answer, or the reader to solve. For instance, the scientist can solve the problem of communication from earth to the moon and beyond, but he has not solved the difficulty of communicating science and engineering to the layman, or the difficulty of communication between individuals. As Bob says in the book, "Space science can help us to see the kind of universe we live in. And as Christians we should want to know because this universe belongs to God . . ."

I found this a very interesting and stimulating book. I hope everybody who reads it enjoys it as much as I did.

Dr. Wilmot N. Hess
Director, Science and Applications
Manned Spacecraft Center
January 10, 1969

PART I

Truth Through Persons

At the End of the Slide Rule

On October 22, 1968 within the NASA community there was in typical earthly fashion a mixture of joy and sadness. In Don Eisele's home a neighbor came by early to express best wishes to the flyer's wife. And then he headed quickly for the hospital where his wife would undergo surgery. His best wishes for his neighbor came off in grand style. A few minutes later her husband landed safely approximately nine hundred nautical miles east of Cape Kennedy. Within forty-six minutes after splash down, the Apollo 7 astronauts were picked up by helicopter pilot Commander Edward Skube, and just twelve minutes later they were on the deck of Aircraft Carrier, U.S.S. Essex.

As I left the happy home where reporters and newsmen by the dozen waited to snap pictures and get quotes, I felt good. But then, not an hour later I found myself in a hospital prayer room with that same man and his son, who earlier in the morning had come by the Eisele home to express concern for the safe return of Apollo 7. Those were a long three hours together as we waited for the surgeon's report.

We talked about many things, including this book. And this man, high in management in our space program, gave this witness: "How comforting it is to see the highly accomplished men in the engineering and scientific community come to our church and to Christ for answers for their lives that they alone do not have nor can explain." He was directing this comment not only to himself, but especially to young engineers and scientists, who, he said, seem to have to go through a doubting, growing up stage before turning to the truth of God. He was right. Our church has many "old heads" in the scientific community who have gone through intellectual gymnastics regarding religion, but they have found their place in the worshiping community of Christians.

Let me emphasize. This witnessing man in that hospital prayer room is by all standards a successful man of science. And then he added: "Tacked onto the end of every slide rule is faith." Where can you go to find a stronger witness than that?

Our prayer sessions were sprinkled with readings from the Holy Bible—at his request. And it helped. Proof of this came later when the surgeons returned and said to him, "Your wife's growths were cancerous."

I could not help but observe that the man had an inner strength that was as real as life itself. Indeed this man, faced with shocking news, had gone beyond the end of the slide rule. And there he had found faith.

As I look back over the events of that day, I see that no community of people exists outside of the total human situation. Simply put, it's like this: the world is a good place in which to live if you accept the fact that while you are having a happy experience, somebody, somewhere is suffering. For every birth, there is a death. For every tragedy there is a joyful occasion. Somewhere along the way in life everyone is going to catch a bit of both. But there are choices for good in all of these situations. When an obvious good comes to our finite minds, we can have an attitude of gratitude; when something strikes our minds as a tragedy, we can *faith our way* through the agony. Faith does not erase the test; it helps us pass it.

After we have tried all the finite answers to our problems, it is strengthening to know that at the end of the slide rule, there is faith.

It Shakes, Rattles, and Rolls

One of the strangest experiences I've ever had came during the years I was working on my instrument ticket. In a link trainer I could feel all of the sensations of flying and still would not be a yard off the ground. This may sound a bit far-fetched to the layman. But a student pilot with two hours will agree it's for real.

How can a person feel he is flying when he is not? Without presuming that anybody could teach or learn instrument flying in "one easy lesson," I will attempt a brief explanation.

When flying an airplane, you keep the wings level by viewing the "level" earth horizon. As you fly into clouds, how can you keep the wings level if there is no longer a visible horizon? At that point you look at an artificial horizon instrument in front of you on the panel. There is a line on that instrument that always stays in a horizontal position. And there are some small "wings" lined up with the artificial horizon which indicate you are flying straight and level. Whenever a "wing" goes up, the airplane is turning in that direction, the compass is changing to a new direction, and the airspeed and altimeter are constant if the nose of the plane is not pitched up or down. A weird thing may happen at this point. When you

5

bring the wings back level and straighten up the airplane, your seat-of-the-pants tells you that you are still in a turn. That phenomenon is called vertigo—you feel you are still in a turn; yet the instruments indicate that you are not. As long as you believe the instruments, you stay alive.

Now the amazing thing about this total experience is that you have the same flying sensations on the ground inside a link trainer. This is a positive use of vertigo, the ability to become disoriented. You are not flying; but you think you are. In letting yourself think you are, you render yourself capable of "flying" on the ground, and in letting yourself go into a turn in the link trainer, you may still have that turning feeling after you've returned to straight and level. That kind of vertigo can get you into trouble when actually flying.

Flight simulation is made possible because a man's mind can fool him. If we couldn't experience vertigo in the air, we couldn't have flight simulation on the ground. In both cases we have to choose, and in choosing, convince ourselves which motions we accept and which ones we do not. Our minds will accept the impressions we choose, making flight simulation a kind of controlled vertigo.

With this description you can imagine something of what it was like when Astronaut Tom Stafford invited me to fill a vacant seat on one of his training exercises aboard the Dynamic Crew Procedures Simulator at NASA. What a ride! What a link trainer does for the airplane pilot, this simulator does for the astronaut—from lift-off to splashdown.

When Tom climbed aboard Apollo 10, I was "there" with him—watching and listening to him as he flipped dozens of switches in checking out his spacecraft. He was so busy doing this last minute checkout that he did not have much time to contemplate his lift-off. I can imagine hearing him say as he pointed to the massive instrument panel, "These goodies have to work before we take off."

Here is what could have happened with his mission because here is what happened with us on different simulated launches. First, the countdown—"mark, 10,9,8,7,6,5,4 (at

6

which time you hear the engines start), 3, ignition,1,0," and she is gone!

Tom kept his left hand on the translation control which can be used at any moment to abort the mission. By triggering this abort handle while on the pad, the abort tower attached to the Command Module will lift the Command Module from the Service Module and shoot the three astronauts 4,000 feet into the air. What a ride that would be! It was rough enough on the simulator.

A loud roar rushes through the ears, the lift-off G's pin you flat against the seat, and you are tumbling at a fantastic rate. Tom responds very quickly, and in using his thrusters he stops the tumbling, gets the blunt end down, ejects the parachutes, and in a rocking motion drifts toward splashdown. On the simulator you get the full rocking effect at the end of parachutes through viewing the shifting artificial horizon outside the simulator on a spherical wall, through onboard instruments, and the actual shifting action of the simulator.

On one of these simulated missions the controller let us go all the way into orbit without causing an emergency situation. Needless to say, I liked that one best! Next to the real thing, this was it. The slow lift-off, the speed acceleration that buries you in your seat, the gradual arc up and over your right shoulder which leaves you looking at this earth's horizon over your shoulders, the surge forward as the first staging event occurs (the forward motion is the craft shifting into a more vertical attitude with the earth), and the deafening silence when the orbit is established—all takes ten minutes and twenty-five seconds.

And when we reentered the atmosphere from orbit, there was a roaring sound "like the 'ch,ch,ch,ch' of a train in the distance," as Tom describes it. The deceleration force in a real flight comes on and builds up to where a 200 pound man would weigh 644 pounds.

Here is how that phenomenon occurs: the astronauts and the spacecraft are traveling a reentry speed of 25,000 mph. In about two minutes the atmosphere pushes back the craft to nearly half that speed. The craft in turn pushes the astro-

7

nauts to a speed equal to the slowing vehicle. With the earth's gravity pulling them down and the atmosphere pushing them back, the astronauts feel "squashed!"

You feel these sensations to a degree in the simulator. And finally, the flight ends as you swing and sway on parachutes to a soft landing.

On other simulated flights the computer controller pulled everything he could think of on Tom. Aborts were made on every phase of the flight into orbit. When Tom climbed out of the simulator following an hour of lift-offs and aborts with all of the roars and tumbling and G's that go with it, the simulator controller commented, "Mr. Stafford, you won't have any trouble." What he was actually saying was, "If you have any trouble, you won't have any trouble handling it." And I believe it.

I can see why he didn't make a launch pad abort on Gemini VI when the lift-off light came on after a premature engine shutdown. A quick cross reference of instruments showed the lift-off light was a fluke. He and his partner kept their cool, made the decision not to abort, and saved a mission. We learned a lot from Gemini VI—we learned that a disciplined man can do what the best equipment cannot do. He can observe, evaluate, and then make decisions.

I can see why he suggested that he go out and kick open the "mouth" of the "angry alligator" on Gemini IX. Controllers at the Center would not permit this and ordered him to stay inside the craft. Tom's self-confidence, born out of a disciplined life, was speaking through that suggestion. The same discipline that prompted his suggestion also caused him to follow the orders that were given him.

All of these things were clearer to me after riding with him on the simulator. His actions were those of a disciplined man.

But now that I think about it, it didn't take that ride to bring out Tom's traits. They can be seen every day in less spectacular ways. When at home, he's in the worship services. Tom is an active steward on our Church's Administrative Board and a trustee on the Edward H. White II Memorial

8

Youth Center. He may be a leader in one situation, a follower in another—but he is dependable in all instances.

On Gemini VI, Wally Shirra captured the headlines with his "Jingle Bells" on the french-harp. Very little was reported of his companion, Tom Stafford. When Tom returned, someone asked how he felt about his partner getting all the attention. His off-the-cuff comment was a typical Stafford answer, "I know I did my job; NASA knows I did my job. That is what matters the most."

Those in a position to know must have recognized Tom's strong sense of discipline. He works just as hard when he is not on a prime crew. That fact had some bearing on his being assigned as the Command Pilot on two backup crews. The backup crew is always just as well prepared as the prime crew. Up until the last minute before lift-off, this backup crew may have to step in and take over.

In Apollo 10 Tom was the pilot in Command. On that mission Tom and Gene Cernan transferred from the Command Module to the Lunar Module. The Lunar Module under Tom's command reduced its orbit to 50,000 feet from the moon's surface; and then swooped back up to rendezvous and dock with the Command Module that was orbiting the moon. There wasn't a lunar landing on that mission, but it was a rehearsal.

These astronauts do only what they are convinced the spacecraft is ready for. If I know Tom, he did exactly what the Lunar Module was capable of doing—nothing more, nothing less.

It may sound ridiculous to say that Astronaut Stafford does not take any chances on a space flight. Risks, yes, but not chances. He is no gambling daredevil; he is a disciplined realist. When Tom says that we are ready for a mission, believe it—we are. If we are not ready, we are not going. And he says so. As the modern cliche goes, he "says it like it really is."

You can simulate a flight; but you cannot simulate the pilot. No machine can take the place of a man who can take orders, and give them—who can make split-second decisions, and take corrective actions accordingly—who can doggedly keep faith with previous commitments. Only man is capable of disciplined life.

While on the simulated flight, I watched the simulator's on-board computer roll off information that kept the mission progressing toward a successful conclusion. Fascinating! But it was the careful, soft touch of the fingers of Astronaut Stafford, the cautions left hand on the abort handle, the bumping of the tumbling craft's thrusters with his right hand, his smooth, confident conversation with the controller—It was this man who gave personality to a ride aboard a roaring, shaking, monster of a machine.

Some people fear that the machine age will dehumanize man. Astronaut Stafford has helped me to understand that man can humanize the best machine. Discipline remains uniquely a human ingredient.

God Hid It

"God hid it from me, but I found it."

Now who made that statement? Was it a nine-year-old who had lost his favorite toy? Or a Sunday school teacher who couldn't find her Scripture lesson in the Bible? Or a devoted old person who had misplaced a keepsake? No, the man who said this is one of our noted space scientists, Dr. P. R. Bell, Director of the Lunar and Earth Sciences Division, whose main job now is to set up and manage the Lunar Receiving Laboratory at the Manned Spacecraft Center.

Twelve years ago at his laboratory with the Atomic Energy Commission at Oak Ridge, Tennessee, he had tried to detect the thorium content of an ordinary meteorite and failed. But on this particular day while a group of us were discussing the idea of writing *Earth, Moon, And Beyond* in a lunch meeting at the Manned Spacecraft Center, P. R., as he is called affectionately by his colleagues, whipped out some pictures and said, "For twelve years God hid it from me, but I found it!" The picture in his hand showed the spectrum of the radiation of thorium.

Now, let's take a closer look at this man's credentials. With this background information, the impact of truth through his witness will come on stronger.

11

Dr. Bell is a native of Ft. Wayne, Indiana, and a graduate of Howard College, Birmingham, Alabama, where he received a Bachelor of Science in 1936 and an Honorary Doctor of Science in 1954.

Following his graduation from Howard College, he was associated with the University of Chicago, where he participated in the installation and the early operation of the Chicago cyclotron in 1941. Dr. Bell later joined the staff of the Massachusetts Institute of Technology Radiation Laboratory where he was involved primarily in radar development.

In 1946 he joined the staff of Union Carbide at the Oak Ridge National Laboratory and began development of, and research with, the scintillation counter, linear amplifiers, and other physics instrumentation developments for low-energy nuclear physics. Dr. Bell's most important earlier contribution to the nation's nuclear program was his work on scintillation counting, a method of radiation detection.

The value of the scintillation counter as developed by Dr. Bell is obvious if one sees a laboratory comparison to the effect that it is one hundred times as sensitive as a beta ray spectrometer and ten to one thousand times as efficient as a Geiger counter in the detection of gamma rays. It is also able to differentiate between types of radiation.

Dr. Bell continued his association with Union Carbide as manager of the DCX-2 project until joining NASA. This experiment is one of the several large complicated devices built to do research on the problem of controlled fusion systems. The DCX machines hold the present record for coming closest to achieving the conditions desired for a thermonuclear burn. The plasma in this machine has the highest temperature and the longest containment time for any of the controlled fusion devices.

Dr. Bell has authored more than sixty articles and three chapters in different books on general radiation field and energetic particles. He attended the World Conference on Atomic Energy in 1958 at Geneva, Switzerland, was a member of the United States team which reviewed Russian thermonuclear work in 1960, and in 1965 he served as a member of the Geochemistry Working Group for the NASA Summer Conference on Lunar Exploration and Science at Falmouth, Mass.

He is a Fellow of the American Physical Society, a member of the Society of Nuclear Medicine, and the American Geophysical Union.

Now that you have an understanding of Dr. Bell's background, his statement, "God hid it from me, but I found it," will take on added meaning. Let me share some further insights of this remarkable man and his personal relationship with God.

For instance, while he was explaining the chemical structure of our earth in terms of gases, I asked him why argon gas acted the way he had described. And he answered, "It's just the way the Lord does it—okay?—It's a deep fact of nature that it just happens that way. You just have to say that it is that way." Then he continues with his fascinating discussion of our earth, the moon, and the universe.

It's obvious that this man is so completely engrossed in what he is doing that he loses himself in his searching experiments. This being the case, I wondered what his answer would be to the direct theological question, "Do you ever think of God in your work?"

He answered, "Oh, when nature hits you on the head with one of these new things—that does it!" And then he continues, "Poor old Bill (Dr. Hess), and me too. We've got so much red tape these days. Oh, brother, it's utterly horrifying, just stack after stack after stack of paper work. I'd like to catch some of those fellows who create this problem and make them handle it." A typically emphatic, yet humorous "P.R." answer.

I then asked if he could remember an experiment where he was shaken to really think about the Being of God.

"Sure, but not so uncommon. Rather frequent, you see. Some of these discoveries are pretty surprising in lots of ways and very interesting. And of course they lead you to think of these things about the Creator. But you don't have to discover them yourselves. Look at these pulsars (discussed in "Little Green Men") we've discovered—utterly astounding,

13

utterly astounding. We don't have the faintest idea what these are. Even the things you comprehend are most remarkable. You take that H_2O—that nice stuff, water. It has one characteristic exceedingly uncommon to other liquids, namely that when it solidifies, the solid is of lower density than the liquid. Now that's most remarkable. Ice floats on top. That is very, very uncommon, I assure you. Yet, if that hadn't been the way that is, there would be no life on this earth."

At this point I asked for further elaboration.

"When the sea freezes, the ice floats on top," he continued. "If it were denser, it would sink to the bottom, and the seas would eventually be completely frozen. If it were not just the way it is, there would be no life on earth."

Throughout all of our conversation the idea is always present that "it's just the way the Lord does it." Any way you cut it, that is a statement of faith.

Some theologians could learn a thing or two about faith from this noted scientist's statement. They seem to argue that God "had" to do something in creation or through Jesus Christ in a certain way. It would be a much more profound statement of faith if we would simply witness from personal experience that "it's just the way the Lord does it." For that is always the case, no matter how little or how much we know about what goes on. And that truth God never hides from us. It's there. All we have to do is accept it.

I Could Be Wrong

I remember the time back in my college days when religion and science were talked about as being at odds. And now the scientific community makes up a large part of my congregation. Certainly not all men of science attend church, any more than do all carpenters, plumbers, college professors, or congressmen. But many of them do. And they are very active within the Christian community. Up to now, I've not met an atheist. A few agnostics, yes, but no atheists.

On the other hand there have been many instances where the scientist's faith in his God was expressed. Some of those times are recorded in this book. The very fact that the invitation to write this book came from within the scientific community at its highest level is in itself proof that men of science are some of our most faithful churchmen. They are Christian scientists in the universal use of the term.

But this fact of a science and religion marriage came to me most strongly one evening as my wife and I were dinner guests along with Dr. and Mrs. Harold Urey in the home of Dr. and Mrs. P. R. Bell. Dr. Urey is highly acclaimed in many areas of science, and to be with Dr. Bell is always a treat.

In 1934, Dr. Harold Urey received the Nobel Prize in chemistry for his discovery of deuterium (heavy hydrogen), made at Columbia University in 1931 with Ferdinand Graft Brickwedde and George Moseley Murphy. He was one of the first to calculate thermodynamic properties from spectroscopic data and was a pioneer in the separation of isotopes, especially by the chemical exchange method. During World War II, he was director of the S.A.M. (war code name) laboratories at Columbia University, where the gas diffusion method for the production of U-235 was developed. In 1945 he was awarded the Medal for Merit.

With the biographical sketches of both Dr. Bell and Dr. Urey in mind, let's go back to that dinner situation. I asked Dr. Urey to tell us about his most exciting accomplishment or discovery. This question brought him to the edge of his chair as he enthusiastically related that experience. And it wasn't his discovery of deuterium. It had to do with a theory that he had set forth twenty years ago. At that time he stated that the moon and the earth did have a similar origin but that the moon did not come from the earth. Analyzed meteorities have revealed a composition like that of the sun. This is also the same composition that the earth must have had in order to be like it is now. We'll know more about this when we bring soil samples back from the moon.

The possibility of water having been on the moon excites Dr. Urey. The earth has extensive sedimentation. Why shouldn't the moon? If those rilles on the moon surface are caused by water, there's a chance that the moon is more soil and less lava. This idea fits Dr. Urey's overall theory of the makeup of the universe. It seems that the possibility of water on the moon is almost fact, as evidenced by the rilles on the lunar surface. But chemical analysis of lunar material will reveal water influence, if there is any.

When I asked why the moon had captured his fancy over the many intriging subjects of modern science, his answer had definite religious overtones. "There is an enormous prejudice among scientists against water on the moon. This caused

16

my interest in it. Astronomers have funny ideas. They ask whether there is water on Mars, whether there is water on Venus; they'll even ask the question about water on Mercury. But the possibility of water having ever been on the moon is never considered."

And then Dr. Urey repeated, "There is an enormous prejudice against water on the moon."

At this point I injected a comment into the conversation: "It seems to me that physicists would have as much to say about the moon's makeup as would the astronomer or geologist."

Dr. Bell answered: "Cosmic thinkers are better fitted for it —characters like this guy here," he nodded toward Dr. Urey and then continued, "have been at it a long time. That's his business."

But Dr. Urey had a wise word here, "When it comes to the moon, there's just nobody that's a specialist."

Our dialogue that evening did not end at this point. But this is a fairly accurate summary of the conversation, and it reveals one religious implication within the scientific community. The greatest of these minds are plagued at times with prejudice. When any person in a search for truth, whether a religious or a scientific search, closes his mind toward another's thoughts, truth itself is denied. A closed mind searching for truth is demonic, and that's a religious problem. Whenever a person closes his mind to another's opinion, he paralyzes his ability to judge. A mind made up is a mind shut down.

A good scientist weighs all the evidence, and on the basis of that evidence makes his judgment. But he must always be open to new evidence. His problem to date is that he does not know all the facts about the universe. But on the basis of what he does comprehend, judgments are made. And it becomes truth even though the scientist doesn't know all about the matter under judgment.

It seems to me that if truth involved an absolute knowledge about any one thing, we could never know it. But we can know a truth about a thing if we are open to any evidence concerning it. Truth is a way, a spirit, an attitude. Jesus Christ says Truth is a "Way." And I believe it is.

When a person opens himself to truth, he will receive it as his trained, natural intelligence permits him to assimilate it. It is our responsibility to choose to train our intelligence and then open our minds to the truth.

In any search for truth, you may interpret certain evidence in different ways. No one method of interpreting any set of circumstances is necessarily finally the only way, and no words spoken or written ever contain the whole truth.

At the close of Dr. Urey's remarks about his moon-earth-origin theory, he said, "Now, I could be wrong."

To which I reply, "No, Dr. Urey, you are not wrong. In the end you might be wrong about some particular aspect of a moon theory, but even then you will be right—right in attitude, right in spirit, right in direction."

Monday Morning Blahs

Because of our sedentary way of life, most of us are not in very good physical condition. Every time I visit the NASA astronaut training facility I am reminded of this unpleasant fact.

The barbells, weights, exercycles, handball courts, tumbling mats—are all silent reminders of one's physical deterioration. If you don't get the message from the vast array of training equipment, you will from astronaut trainer Joe Garino, an Air Force Master Sergeant on loan to NASA since the start of Project Mercury. Joe is a quiet man. His comments on physical fitness, or the lack of it, are very much to the point, but he never forces himself or his ideas on anyone. He simply puts himself in a position to be used by the astronauts. Joe is there to help, but the astronauts must ask for it.

They are told, "You fly as long as you are physically fit." Needless to say, they ask Joe for assistance in their physical fitness program. And he gives it according to each man's particular need. There is a special exercise for each type of weakness, and each man concentrates on his own physical problem. In this program they do not become super-muscle-men. They simply keep the kinks worked out.

The astronauts carry lightweight exercising equipment aboard the spacecraft for use in flight. The body becomes lazy in weightlessness, the blood pools in the legs, the cardiovascular system slows down, muscle weight is lost, and a calcium deficiency develops. These changes occur as the body adapts to its new environment, but these adaptations are not considered hazardous in a weightless condition. However, the astronaut must return to earth, and unless he keeps fit by daily onboard exercise, discomfort may be experienced upon return to earth. Normal health in a weightless environment is abnormal health on earth. This is why the astronaut must be kept as close to normal earth health as possible. We have discovered, according to Dr. Charles Berry, NASA'S top physician, that complete adaptation to the earth environment comes again to the astronaut within a few days after his return from a flight. But normal earth health is regained more through physical exercise than through any other known factor. And he feels better.

I know from first hand experience that Joe's methods work. A year ago I went to him, overweight and weak—looking much like one on the TV commercial with the "Monday morning blahs." He outlined a plan of exercise, and I went to work. Up to this time my primary concern had been to exercise my mind, but now I make sure that mind *and* body get exercise. And I've never felt better.

Authorities insist that the mind affects the body, and I believe it does. But Joe feels that the opposite is true also—the body affects the mind. He says: "I believe that the mind and body have to be one. They must be united."

Joe's thesis applies to the astronauts, to me—to you. "For his mental well-being, a person needs to be physically fit." When you say, after flexing some muscles, "I've never felt better," it may be because your mind has received signals from a healthy body. That alert body makes *you* feel good.

What can we do to regain our lost strength and vitality? We can follow the astronauts' program. After weighing in, they run a mile or more. Next, they do whatever special exercise is needed for their specific weak spot, and then comes a "free play period" where they square off against each other in friendly sports competition. With variations, this exercise schedule can become our action plan for good physical and mental health.

Joe Garino says, "The hardest part is getting off the chair the first time." That doesn't take much physical strength, but it takes will power triggered by a driving desire.

We do have an alternative. We can sit and look blah! Or we can run for our lives.

I'm running.

Negative Success

The big daddy of the Apollo Command Module spacecraft is Mr. Kenneth Kleinknecht. His experiences in designing supersonic aircraft from scratch make him an authority on how to succeed with a project. His successes were many as Mercury Project Manager and as assistant Gemini Project Manager.

He succeeds because he understands failure. In a brand new design there is always a weak spot, a malfunction, a failure. He knows that something can go wrong—at some point the system may fail. But that failure does not defeat the project. It defeats itself by revealing itself, thereby permitting the problem to be corrected.

He puts it this way: "Some of our biggest strides forward have come out of failures. What some people call failures, we call negative successes." Let's look at a couple of negative successes. A "hung thruster" opens up the way to a solution to that problem. "Malfunctioning breaker switches" point to a problem, and to an ultimate solution. A hundred failures can help us see a hundred ways that something won't work. And that knowledge helps find a way that will work.

When you think about it, what he says makes sense for every life situation. We all know what it means to fail; if we

22

haven't failed, we haven't lived. But we know that it's the keep-on-keeping-on attitude in spite of failure that makes any success possible.

Maybe this is the reason why our nation has come so far in so little time in the space race—we have taken our failures —the tragic Apollo fire being the worst—and learned from them. As long as we do that, these so-called failures are indeed *negative successes*. It's when we give up, quit trying, lose our initiative, that we truly fail.

This is why our nation has no alternative except to go forward in our conquest of space. We can take the failures that prod us on to success, but we cannot endure the failures that we give in to. Failure is not the supreme tragedy—that occurs only when we succumb to failure and no longer try to succeed. When the will to succeed is gone, little else matters.

For example, the early Apollo holocaust that took the lives of our three astronauts was a national tragedy. But, if we haven't learned from that accident, a far greater tragedy will have occurred. If we haven't learned that anxious hurrying costs time, they will have died in vain. If we haven't learned from the fire that life is our most precious and fragile possession, the sacrifice of these men will count for nothing. If we haven't learned that our national grief was a blessing, a greater tragedy has happened to us. For a grieving nation is a loving nation, and only those who love are capable of grief. In our moments of tragedy and bereavement, if we have become acutely aware of the voice of a loving God Who calls us together as one family under His Fatherhood, our ill-fated space pioneers will not have died in vain.

But, the phenomenal success of our continuing Apollo space program indicates that we have learned from the tragedy. Our technology has put us back on schedule with a sophisticated spacecraft—as fireproof as you can get it and with all the comforts of home. We have learned that the human component in our space effort is far more important than the time factor. Kenneth Kleinknecht comments, "We've got a good spacecraft now; very little will be done to modify it. Something must really be wrong before we change it. Because in changing

23

something, you can cause bigger problems elsewhere." So it looks like the early failures in the Apollo Command Module have produced positive results—we learned how to develop a spacecraft capable of carrying three men to the moon and back.

No, our failures in the space effort have not been in vain and where we go from here is anybody's guess at the moment. In our relentless pursuit of space knowledge, we may yet face future mistakes and tragedy—a mission may yet be rubbed out. Accidents can occur anywhere—on the freeway, in the air, or in outer space. Failures—negative successes—are very much a part of life. They direct us toward our goal, toward fulfilment, toward the positive success we all look for in personal experience and in national effort.

Scratching at the Edge of the Unknown

When I showed a picture of the Lunar Excursion Module (LM) to a friend, he exclaimed, "If there is anyone on the moon, that thing will scare him to death!" Now, we know there is no one on the moon for this "spider" to scare, but, admittedly, the LM does look a bit unusual. As a matter of fact, I have had the opportunity to "ride" in the LM simulator at the Manned Space Center. This was a most informative and exciting venture. With the aid of advanced TV and electronic devices, the simulated ride becomes the "real" thing. It is an unbelievably amazing and unusual journey—demanding an equally amazing and unusual craft.

Of necessity this flying "space bug" *must* look like it does. We need a module with a gimballed landing engine that can be pointed down in various directions. This is essential in order to maneuver for a landing. And it is important to have angled windows that will permit the lunar astronauts to look down on the surface of the moon. Antennas, jutting out in weird formation, are fundamental for spacecraft communications and the grotesque leg assemblies were engineered to fold up so that the unsymmetrical craft could fit inside the rocket assembly. Combine these and many other necessary components and the result is the LM. There's never been a

Ascent stage of the Lunar Module lifting off for a rendezvous with the orbiting Command Module

flying machine like it before simply because the needs have not been present.

Will this LM do the job it was designed for? I raised this question with General Carroll H. Bolender, the "big daddy" of the flying space bug. He is responsible for the management of the Lunar Module Program, including design, development, and fabrication of the vehicle by the Grumman Aircraft Engineering Corporation, the LM prime contractor. General Bolender predicted that the LM would do the job for which it was designed. But the major question at this point is: what if a need develops that the hardware was not equipped to handle? If there is one concern that General Bolender and his associates have regarding the LM's capabilities, this is it. Is there some unknown factor that will enter into a manned lunar landing that we do not know about? We must realize that, while this is not likely, it is a possibility. The LM has to function 232,000 miles from home under conditions that we cannot completely simulate here on earth. The unknown remains the mission's biggest threat—the LM is scratching against the edge of the unknown.

This is a space age example of man's constant predicament. The more knowledge that is acquired, the greater his awareness of the unknown. This is the essence of wisdom.

Man's knowledge is always relative to his ignorance, not to infinite knowledge. Infinite knowledge belongs to the Creator. What creature, whose fragile life is a mere heartbeat from the grave, would dare compare his knowledge with God's?

But, we do not believe that landing on the moon is an intrusion upon knowledge that belongs only to the Creator. His knowledge surpasses ours to an infinite degree. But we can start with the knowledge that others have given us and build on it. Our scientific and technical "know-how" is God-given, and our itch for the unknown is a response to the life force breathed into man by his Creator.

We don't mind LM's scratching at the edge of the unknown, but we do hope we've scratched out enough knowledge to land on the moon. From the lunar surface we will be able to scratch further into the unknown—as God wills.

27

Closing the Gap

For years we watched airplanes glide on wings through the skies. Then, quite suddenly, we can hardly believe our eyes—on our television screens we see men perched atop a rocket, which goes off like a large bullet with a slow start.

It is quite likely that most of us were unaware of the experimental transition between the airplane, fitted for the atmosphere, and the ballistic capsule, suitable for space flight. The in-between stage—part-airplane and part-capsule—is the supersonic X-15 that never takes off from the ground. Lashed to the bottomside of a B-52 wing, the X-15 is already flying at a high speed before it starts on its own.

Astronaut Joe Engle, with sixteen X-15 flights behind him, seems to be the logical one to listen to concerning some of the changes that accompany the spanning of the atmosphere-to-space gap. While Joe would insist he is not an expert, I find his comments on the subject quite enlightening.

In flight, test pilot Joe Engle would climb into his small-but-powerful X-15 snuggled under the B-52 wing, ignite his engine upon release by the mother ship, put the experimental craft into a climb angle at a top speed of 2,196 nautical miles per hour, and after engine burn-out would carry on ballistically over the top. Proper use of reaction controls, similar to the thrusters on space Command Modules, keep the craft from tumbling as it goes "over the top" at an altitude of 53½ miles. The X-15's re-entry attitude, reached by bumping the thrusters, must be established by the time the craft falls back to 180,000 feet, otherwise a buffeting by the denser atmosphere would cause loss of control.

Joe's X-15 flights barely left the denser atmosphere on a short arch into space. His craft went from more to less and then back to more atmosphere. In the "pure" space of the orbiting spacecraft there are scattered molecules of atmosphere. Speaking of the atmosphere molecule in outer space, Joe says, "It goes sailing out there and bumping around while still in the earth's gravity."

Orbit decay, space language that describes the satellite's lowering until it returns to earth, is caused by these minute molecules gradually knocking the craft back to a slower speed, thereby permitting the earth's gravitational pull to be greater than the craft's centrifugal force.

Judging from these boundary flight experiences, one would inevitably assume that we need a ballistic capsule that can perform with thrusters in the farther distances of space on the one hand, while on the other hand, it must have a lifting body characteristic which will provide some kind of guidance within the more dense atmosphere. We now need an "aerospace craft" that can fly or orbit at the will of the pilot, and that design is in the making.

By the time man gets this transitional craft perfected, it will be antiquated; and a new one will be in the making. As one technological gap closes; another opens. And the cycle is endless.

But not all these gaps are technological. Some are situational. For instance, capsule flying proved to be a big change from the former days of aircraft flight only. In longer duration capsule flying, man has had to set up housekeeping! Man, in flying off into the wild black yonder to escape household chores, has wound up where he left—housekeeping!

Joe Engle says, "It's a long way from a ten minute X-15 flight to a ten day orbit." But it seems ten times longer when

29

you consider the mundane chores of emptying the waste-basket, keeping the "toilet" clean, preparing TV dinners, and tucking away every item that might clutter up the capsule space by floating around.

In time even that gap will close. Housekeeping will be carried on in orbiting space stations like it is on earth, and short duration flights will carry astronauts to and from these stations. By then we will be on our way to Mars—and beyond, demanding more housekeeping for longer periods.

In closing one gap, we open another one. Or rather, another one opens itself. In either case we find ourselves constantly having to bridge gaps. This fact of modern technology spotlights one of man's dilemmas. He is forever bridging gaps—credibility gaps, educational gaps, talent gaps. In a sense, this constitutes a heavy burden, but without it there could be no challenge. We are just human enough to resist being thankful for gaps, which in many instances may be evil, but it is a real thrill to meet the challenge of the gaps, and close a few.

Ed's Space Gun—And an Engineer

A NASA assistant administrator on the top floor of the tallest building in the Houston complex looked out through his wall of glass and reminisced about how he had grown with NASA in the last ten years. He had traveled a long and lonely road from a machine shop across the way to this plush, ninth-floor office.

But the thing that meant the most to him during this ten-year-period was not this expansive office, private secretary, and the public prestige that goes with his position. The one event that meant the most to him was that two-month, day-and-night project of designing and building the space gun used by Astronaut Ed White on our first space walk. *He* helped engineer and put together the first space gun. Obviously, his involvement in that endeavor meant more to him than meeting and entertaining the highest dignitaries, than his higher salary, than the status of his high office.

When Ed White stepped out into space, it was a big moment for everybody. But when he squeezed that space gun's trigger, he really "turned on" a young engineer. As Ed maneuvered around by the thrust of the space gun, this young engineer moved just as lightly on earth. His space gun was a success. And this made him a success, too.

31

That seems to be the case with most successful persons. Success in any personal endeavor produces a sense of well-being. But, nobody succeeds who doesn't try, who doesn't involve himself, who doesn't pitch in and give it all he's got.

This is why every so-called "little man" concerned with manned space flight—every wire twister, every riveter, every screw turner is elated over each successful space flight. His wires, rivets, and screws stood their test. So, he passed his test!

There's no end to the number of lives that can share the feeling of success which comes by involvement. The one who works the hardest usually experiences the most success. He may not make as much money as his less industrious neighbor, but he "accomplishes" more.

This is just another way of expressing the time proven paradox: the more of yourself you give in life, the more you receive from life. To enjoy your work—give it all you've got!

An Astronaut's Search

What motivates an astronaut to ride on top of a mountain of blasting fire, withstand the gravity forces trying to pull him through his couch back to earth, egress from his vehicle for a walk in space, and upon reentry lay on a heat shield that is ten times hotter than the hottest frying pan?

I'm sure we've all wondered about this. So, I asked Astronaut Leroy Gordon Cooper why he looked forward to a lunar space flight. His reaction was amazing, "I look forward to the lunar space flight—and beyond!" Cooper's quiet confidence made the statement sound as if it shouldn't be questioned. And I didn't question.

Astronaut Cooper continued, "There are many reasons. But, first and foremost, man has always explored space. Even before he could read and write, he was exploring the world about him, migrating across continents. Later he penetrated the depths of the jungles, climbed the great mountains, and fought his way through Antarctic blizzards to the South Pole. He built devices to explore the subminiature world, then theorized on what was too small to examine even with the most powerful microscopes. He built larger and larger telescopes to penetrate the universe, and then theorized on what was beyond his reach. In short, man was born with an insatiable curiosity to learn more about himself and the universe about him. He has always been an explorer, and he always will be."

Then Cooper switched from third to first person and continued, "I will treasure my American heritage and will do all I can to preserve and enrich it . . . I will acquire the exploring attitude that seeks the truth in all things and adventure on the frontiers of our changing world."

When Astronaut Cooper said "I will acquire the exploring attitude that seeks the truth in *all* things," he did not know that this was actually my mission in writing this book—the search for Truth is everybody's search—the astronaut's, the minister's, the cabbie's, the secretary's, the construction worker's. . . . Gordon Cooper has carried his search for Truth into space, and He experienced what Jesus Christ said could be found by anyone, anywhere—if we look.

"Seek and ye shall find; knock and it shall be opened unto you."

An Answer to the Cosmonaut

Recently, Col. L. Gordon Cooper gave his Christian witness before a youth group at Seabrook Methodist Church. Here are his words: "When asked what I thought about the statement Yuri Gagarin made about not finding God in space, I replied, 'I didn't anticipate finding God up there. If you haven't found God here on earth, you wouldn't find Him in space.' God is everywhere—not in one particular place.

"I have been asked if my Christian faith helped in facing the risks that go with being an astronaut—yes, it certainly has. Especially when you are lying in the spacecraft on the launch pad, faith in God is comforting and sustaining. There is a relative calm to what it would be if I didn't have faith. Actually the launch is not terrifying at all; it is enjoyable and satisfying because of my faith. Then, when you get into the last phase of the countdown—10,9,8,7,6,5,4,3,2,1—anxiety is greatly alleviated because of faith."

If this statement of faith doesn't negate the Russian Cosmonaut's comment about "no God up there," nothing can. In fact, a comparison of the two statements causes us to feel a bit sympathetic toward the hollow soul who boasts about not finding God in outer space.

I suspect that Gagarin's statement was nothing more than

the usual Communist "party line" and was repeated in blind conformity to an atheistic culture. The statement has the ring of something canned, whether what he said was written on paper or washed into his brain.

Two astronauts were whirling in space. One says, "I don't see God up here." And the other one said:

"Father, thank You, especially for letting me fly this flight. Thank You for the privilege of being able to be in this position; to be up in this wondrous place, seeing all these many startling, wonderful things that You have created.

"Help guide and direct all of us that we may shape our lives to be much better Christians, trying to help one another, and to work with one another rather than fighting and bickering. Help us to complete this mission successfully. Help us in our future space endeavors that we may show the world that a democracy really can compete, and still are able to do things in a big way, and are able to do research and development, and can conduct many scientific and very technical programs.

"Be with all our families. Give them guidance and encouragement, and let them know that everything will be okay.

"We ask in Thy Name. Amen"*

There is the answer concerning the whereabouts of God. He's in man's soul. Wherever that Spirit-filled soul goes, there goes God.

---

*This prayer was given by Astronaut Leroy Gordon Cooper, Jr. as he orbited the earth during the flight of Mercury spacecraft Faith 7.

Medicine's Frontier

Space exploration is the frontier of our times.

Frontiers always reveal new scenery, new challenges, new ideas, new ways of looking at old problems. And the space frontiers of today are not exceptions. Perhaps no frontier better characterizes this fact than does space medicine.

Until the recent thrusts by man into space, the primary emphasis of medicine was to make a sick person well—space medicine takes a well person and tries to keep him that way. This approach was inevitable because man's health must be maintained in such alien environments as weightlessness and varying G forces. Because of this space-age necessity, preventive medicine as an actual practice with persons was truly born. The astronaut "patients" are a normal, exceptionally healthy group of men.

The space doctors are men of medicine in our universities across the country, in medical centers, and at NASA—all under the direction of Dr. Charles Berry, head of aerospace medicine. Dr. Berry was one of the first men to enter this highly specialized field. While still an Air Force lieutenant colonel, he helped select the first seven Mercury astronauts and set up the medical monitoring stations in the world-wide spacecraft tracking network. Dr. Berry resigned his commission in 1962 to work full time for the space agency, and he is now the nation's leading space physician.

In a conversation with Dr. Berry about space medicine, he commented, "In our early space flights we proved to the world that man could live in space. Not only that, but we soon proved he could adapt himself to that environment. In space we saw man readjust his cardiovascular system. There was a pooling of the blood in the lower parts of the body, and that system grew lazy because it didn't have to work.

"Before our first manned flight, I received calls throughout the night from men of medicine and science who begged me not to go through with it. They insisted that men would be killed out there. . . . This can be a mighty lonely business at times."

Unquestionably, frontier decision makers do have their lonely moments. Dr. Berry reflected for a few moments and then continued, "We have had some calcium loss, but not enough to limit the missions. Most of these things are signs of adaptation. The astronauts adapt to a zero G environment, and there are no difficulties while they are in space. They don't suffer from motion sickness because of their test pilot experience. Their systems are already adapted to spins and all sorts of relative motion. You might call this a 'downhill adaptation.' Actually, this adaptiveness is due not only to weightlessness but to the total experiences of the mission of which weightlessness plays a big part. . . . We try to provide an environment in which the astronaut can live, and the environment we can't provide, he adapts to. . . ."

When I actually had the opportunity to think through Dr. Berry's comments, some rather startling truths began to take shape. It seems clear that man is more adaptive to different environments than we had ever dreamed. Thanks to man's adaptive powers, what the doctors cannot do for the astronauts in space to keep them "earth fit," man's body will take care of when he returns to earth. Within days he's back to normal! Earth normal, that is.

Now, this ability to adapt cannot have been an accident.

God made us this way, and I believe He means for us to make use of our inate adaptive powers.

However, we know that we cannot thrust men out into raw space environment without any protection. That would be foolish. So, God and man must join hands in partnership in the frontier of space medicine. (As we should in all frontiers.) It is the responsibility of space doctors to determine the adaptive powers of man. And in doing this, they are discovering to some measure the Creator's involvement in the frontier.

But God is a partner more than just in the matter of man's adaptive powers. It is He who gives us the intelligence to protect ourselves in a different environment; it is He who has given us our curiosity; it is He who has established our frontiers and then helps us move ahead toward them.

I believe this God-man partnership is essential to taming every frontier within this amazing universe of ours. God's laws cannot be broken without serious consequence. It is up to us to discover His laws and cooperate with them—with Him.

It is comforting to know that the health and well-being of our astronauts come under the care of Dr. Charles Berry. There is a human-divine partnership here that I have sensed on many occasions. This can best be illustrated by relating a personal conversation in which I commented concerning an election, "It'll be too late for prayer if that man's elected." He answered, "Brother Bob, it's never too late for prayer."

That statement reveals something of the man's spiritual depth.

Someone Who Cares

If you were watching television on the day of splashdown for Apollo 7, you saw a man step up to the door of the helicopter the moment it landed on the deck of the Essex. It was Dr. Don Stullken, the man responsible for planning the recovery.

The astronauts were in the hands of the recovery forces from the time the chutes opened until they were returned safely to the Cape. It was right that he should greet them first.

In a conversation Dr. Stullken reminded me of the fact that there was a large complement of men out there on the water and in the air that day who were responsible for the recovery. However, there is no question in my mind that Dr. Stullken was a big influence in bringing about a safe recovery.

The recovery force consists of an aircraft carrier, an assortment of other ships, helicopters, and conventional aircraft—all functioning under many watchful eyes. But I feel Dr. Stullken looked on in a very special way.

This dedicated man means business. He is deeply concerned for the safety of each astronaut and for every member of the recovery forces. He says, "We never want to place any member of the recovery forces in a more hazardous situation than is absolutely necessary commensurate with the safety of the astronauts."

What goes on during recovery? Let Dr. Stullken tell it in his own way.

"Did we think of everything? Is there something else? Will something go awry? And when the words come, 'We've got the spacecraft in sight,' what a relief! Whew, what a relief! After that instant, everything that follows is really anticlimactic.

"The euphoric feeling is highly contagious. You can't help but get right into the spirit of the whole thing with the astronauts. They sort of set the tenor for the entire recovery group. There were 2600 men aboard the Essex. Obviously, I didn't talk with all of them, but of the 1000 or 1500 men whose expressions I saw, everyone was wearing a grin from ear to ear and was proud of the small part he had to play in it. Then, when the astronauts cut the celebration cake, the emotion was really contagious. You couldn't help but respond emotionally—some laughed, others cried.

"Three years ago when we were on the Boxer in the Atlantic Ocean waiting for word on Gemini VIII—they developed a problem and had to land in the South Pacific. There was a period of time when we knew they were in trouble, but there wasn't a cotton pickin' thing we could do to help. How was this going to turn out? This was the first problem requiring early termination of a mission that we had. What a tremendous sense of relief when the word came through the channels that the parachutes were sighted!"

Dr. Stullken continues his description of the emotional buildup of the recovery forces before and during a mission: "You sail. You go through the training sessions, and then you go out and do the job at sea.

"When launch day arrives, the tension gets terribly high.

"They tease me about saving money by walking sixteen inches off the deck! Secretly, you wish this was only a five-day-mission instead of eleven days.

"About twenty-four to thirty-six hours before recovery you begin to ask, 'Have we practiced enough? Have we forgotten

41

something? What can happen to us at this point that can keep us from providing the level of support we are supposed to give?'

"You hear the words, 'retro fire', over the radio, and boy, that's an interminable twenty minutes from retro fire to main chute. Then comes that great sense of relief when you hear the voices of the astronauts again.

"When Apollo 7 landed we lost communication with the craft. Not a word came through from them. You try to convince yourself everything's all right. You keep thinking, 'It could turn upside down, and if it does, it will take a little while to come rightside up again.' You keep telling yourself that there is no need to be worried, but you are worried and the tension is terrific. Then the spacecraft rights itself. The beacons resume sending signals, and you hear the astronaut talking to one of the helicopters by radio. What a relief! That's when the whole ship goes wild.

"Some of the things we do before and during recovery are different from normal ship procedures. There are periods of conflicts with ideas and concepts. I don't have the authority to order them to do a thing. But I can make some pretty strong recommendations!

"There are times when the need for additional training is not accepted enthusiastically by all concerned. Or again, when the concern of some people leads them to recommend training to a point where you begin to worry that they may get stale or wear out the equipment. It's difficult for people doing this job for the first time to have a 'feeling' for when it seems to be right. But when you've been on a large number of these recoveries, you begin to get that feeling—you are able to provide guidance. And that's our job—to guide operations.

"If you get caught in a bind and something unfortunate happens through no fault of the recovery forces, you can bet your bottom dollar that every Monday morning quarterback that knows what we did will say, 'Maybe they should have practiced some more.'

"But, let me make one point clear. We NASA people enjoy excellent rapport at all levels with the Department of Defense forces. They deserve the credit; we just contribute to it."

"Following the recovery of Apollo 7, the captain of the ship asked, 'Doc, how's your humor today?'

"I responded, 'I could never feel better. Everything has gone just right. We got them aboard.'

"That's not what I asked. How's your sense of humor?"

"I suspected there was something in the wind. That evening they had a big dinner for the astronauts in the Ward Room. First, the executive officer introduced each of the astronauts, and then made a little speech. Next, he introduced the admiral, and then he presented the captain of the ship. The captain glanced my way and I had an uneasy feeling that I was about to discover the reason for his concern about my humor that day. He read a citation that inducted me into the Order of the Gorilla.

"This will take some explanation. They had an innovation that I have never seen on any other ship. Apparently, this idea was thought up by the Catholic chaplain. They had what they called 'The Gorilla' (It was probably the chaplain himself.). Everybody on board knew The Gorilla's telephone number, and if some junior seaman was unhappy with his lot, he could always get it off his chest by calling The Gorilla. It's a kind of a crying towel sort of thing. Well, the Order of the Gorilla is composed of people who create problems for The Gorilla.

"He said that I merited it on three counts: One, I was a scene stealer—it seems that I had inserted, not just my ugly mug, but the unlovely back of my bald head into all of the good photographs, thereby detracting from our nation's space heroes. Two, I had raised the ambient noise level in the ship and created confusion by generating an excessive number of calls on the public address system for my lost NASA personnel. Three, the spot 'I' had selected for recovery was the center of a rain storm, thereby making the whole operation more difficult.

"The citation was accompanied by the presentation of a

43

big powder puff—a huge pom-pom full of powder. Then the captain proceeded to tell the crew how they happened to select this particular gift. He said he went down to the ship's stores officer and asked, 'What item in this store do you have that sells slower than anything else?'

"The officer pointed to this powder puff and said, 'We've had four of these things for three years and never sold a one' —it was the most worthless thing they had!

"Everybody had a lot of fun. And I accepted my citation in the same spirit that it was given."

After hearing Dr. Stullken's intellectual and emotional commitment to his job, and after feeling his keen sense of responsibility, as well as his good humor—I decided that if I were an astronaut, I'd want a man associated with my recovery from space to be just like Don Stullken. I'd want a man who cared.

In every life venture this remains a universal need. We need the assurance that there is someone who cares.

Self-Sacrifice

The NASA community of space people live under great stress. Some can take it, and stay with it; others cannot and feel they must change jobs.

But I have a hunch that stress and strain has a way of following all of us around, no matter what jobs we hold.

Actually, every situation is different. Some people have overextended themselves and are not up to the job they have. Others want out because their particular job is not enough of a challenge. The insecurity that an uncooperative Congress might give by failing to make needed appropriations is another reason for looking for greener pastures. Undoubtedly, the pressure is greatest when tests must meet a deadline prior to a launch. Being a pastor in this highly mobile area, I naturally hear a great deal about the pressures. That's my calling—to listen to problems.

But, my close association with many of the NASA people has given me the opportunity to monitor attitudes, and I am happy to report that from the gym janitor to the top scientist there is tremendous enthusiasm for the job they are doing. For example, the scientists in the Lunar Receiving Laboratory are so devoted to their task that they are opening themselves

45

to the possibility of being quarantined for life. This may seem to be only a remote possibility, but it could happen! I have discovered that many of the heads of the various divisions of responsibility actually took a reduction in salary when they went to work in the lunar landing program. And the more experienced astronauts could be millionaires if they were willing to withdraw from the program and accept a more lucrative position.

Their devotion to the cause certainly shakes up our society's value system where the dollar means so much. It was that devotion that called and kept in the lunar program the three astronauts who perished in the Apollo fire. Ed White, Gus Grissom, and Roger Chaffee did not have to be where they were on that fateful day. They could have chosen safer environs, but they were devoted to their calling. While Chaffee never made a space flight, he risked his life every week in preparation. Grissom had blasted off the pad before on Mercury IV and Gemini III, and Ed White was America's first space walker. What makes a man commit his life to such untried adventures? They felt the venture was worthwhile—so worthwhile that they were willing to take the risks.

These dedicated people could *teach* us a few things about life. Do we feel that what we are doing is worthwhile? So worthwhile that we are willing to risk our lives? If we had the opportunity of doubling our income, would we stay where we are? Each of us must give his own answer.

It seems to me that if what we are doing is worthwhile it must stand up under this three question test: *Is it worthwhile to my Creator?* After all, He put me here, and He ought to have something to say about what I am doing. *Is it worthwhile for others?* Others include future generations as well as those living now. *Is it worthwhile for me?*

I believe that our efforts are meaningful to us if we are convinced that our job is worthwhile to our Creator and others. Consequently, we must first get in tune with God's will. If our job is creative, then our energies are directed into the right channels. As NASA's men of science keep reminding me, God continues to create. As long as we are positively creating

46

(that means for good), God is in it. And if what we are doing is creative, others will feel that our activities are worthwhile. They will reap benefits from our labor, even as we have a right to reap from their labor.

Self-fulfillment involves commitment to others and to God. There is no other way—it is the way of love and service. This is why people sacrifice time, money, and self. They feel that what they are doing is worthwhile and lasting.

Apollo 7

On October 11, 1968, astronauts Donn Eisele, Wally Shirra, and Walt Cunningham lifted off the launch pad at Cape Kennedy into earth orbit and tested the Command Module for it's coming trip to the moon.

In a way, I could visualize a little bit of what was happening because several months before the Apollo 7 flight I "flew" with Donn Eisele in a simulator at the Manned Spacecraft Center. Having flown almost four hundred hours in simulated flight or in actual instrument conditions, I had some idea as to what to expect, but this particular experience was quite a thrill. You actually feel and experience every sensation of flight—yawing, turning, pitching, while "orbiting" the earth. The craft's instruments send signals through the eyes to the brain, and you can feel the results of the pilot's response.

After the required amount of time in "orbit," the flight plan to rendezvous with a target vehicle was implemented. A computer indicated how long to burn thrusters in order to put us into the same "orbit" as the target vehicle. This was accomplished by expanding our "orbit" so that we would come up under the target vehicle. On that day's trial run, Donn let me sit in the command pilot's seat as we maneuvered to within two miles of the target vehicle. This particular simulator does not have the capability of moving closer to the target. For a time we "floated" underneath the target vehicle and then we went on in our "orbit," leaving it behind.

As we moved away, I experienced my strangest reaction of the "flight." Caught up as I was in an emotional involvement in the rendezvous mission, I actually felt there were men out there in the vehicle who were being left behind. And it was a most disturbing feeling.

This made me appreciate all of the backup systems that are built into the spacecraft to minimize failure potential of all kinds, including inability to link up with a target vehicle. If one way of controlling this craft goes out, there's another one to try. For every valve, switch, transistor, tube, or wire, there is a substitute. You don't have to "fly the simulator" to be impressed with these precautions, but it helps.

I was impressed with the emphasis on safety and was grateful to know that our country's leaders are not willing to get to the moon at the expense of the lives of our astronauts. Nothing preempts the safety of the men aboard the spacecraft. The proof of this statement comes from the fact that our astronauts watch the spacecraft as it is assembled and make suggestions in perfecting the module. They will fly only after being convinced that the vehicle is ready to go. And no one forces them to say "yes."

Such care and concern on the part of the thousands of participants of every launch implants confidence into the astronauts themselves. *Care and concern*—both words express deep spiritual feelings. As long as we care enough and show that concern, confidence from within our space community will be maintained. Everyone needs somebody who cares— the scientific community is no exception.

Heroes

Thirty years ago the motion picture star was a public hero —today, the astronaut is the hero. But there seems to be a marked difference between the two types. The actor was the public's hero, and he (or she) played the part in real life in the same way he acted on the screen. This public role playing set them apart in the admiring spectator's mind.

Today, astronauts are admired by the entire world, but they do not play a role—they are just themselves wherever you see them. After a successful space mission, when people get that "touch you" feeling, they just mingle and mix like ordinary folks. While their space TV has been quite spectacular, their everyday attitude is very ordinary. If one of them should start acting like a star, the rest would probably laugh him right out of his space underwear!

Many of these space heroes are shy types who let their deeds speak for themselves. But then they tone down their own accomplishments by insisting that each mission is the result of the dreams and efforts of many people.

Possibly this is why they are a unique breed of heroes—a kind we haven't seen in the past. They insist that over 400,000 workers and millions of taxpayers share in their conquests, and they acknowledge the fact that a vast human effort has provided them with the opportunity to perform their historic feats. It seems to me that our astronauts typify a new breed of hero—they do not set themselves apart from the rest of us; they include us, give us credit, and make us feel important. They make it easy for us to identify with what they are doing. The greatest of these men do not consider themselves super-human. And they tell you so. Yes, here is a new and refreshing kind of hero.

Those who are openly committed to God reveal an authentic form of humility. This is not to say that they are without problems. Not at all—they readily admit it, and it is this honest openness that makes them so human.

To the public, today's astronauts are symbols of greatness. They have done what we would like to do but cannot. In the meantime they are acting in our behalf . . . and giving us some of the credit!

But the authentic quality of their lives is not limited to an academic appraisal of their personalities. It is revealed by the impact of their lives on others. Millions cheer the astronaut because they have been made to feel better and stronger by his accomplishment. Anyone who can inspire that emotion just has to be a hero—the applause received is small compared to what is given.

The Real Heroes

While the astronauts receive—and rightly so—a tremendous amount of public acclaim, they, in turn, pay homage to the supporting scientists, engineers, and technicians who back them up by giving them the technological ingredients for success.

But, I have come to believe that the real heroes are the wives—wives of astronauts, scientists, medical doctors, engineers, technicians, etc.

These wives and mothers have given, and given, and given. While their husbands work seventeen hours a day to meet deadlines, these mothers are working at being parents, and in many cases that means "father" as well as mother. At times they must feel they are married to phantoms who fly in and out of their lives by chance. True, their marriages are built on faith, but I'm sure that every now and then they would like to see just who it is they must have faith in!

While reflecting on these heroines of the home front, I ran into Trudy Cooper, wife of Astronaut Gordon Cooper. She commented casually, "Today I'm a painter!" This is just one example of the multiplicity of chores she must perform to keep the home together and going.

The experiences of these wives point dramatically to a

truth we may overlook: the spotlight is not always on the real hero. She may be standing in the shadows; not always agreeing, but never complaining; lonely, but not ungrateful; tired, but not faint. Turn the spotlight on her and she would be embarrassed. I salute the "real heroes" of our space program. Their courage is an inspiration to even greater achievement.

Man's Inequality and Equality

There is a vacuum chamber in the Lunar Receiving Laboratory at the Manned Spacecraft Center that was designed by Dr. P. R. Bell. It is an almost unbelievable piece of equipment, but Dr. Bell insists that there are thousands of others who could have developed it.

In broad terms (very broad!), here is how it works. Large pumps carry gas molecules out of the vacuum area and leave as much of nothing in there as is possible. Actually there is only one ten-billionth of an amount of ordinary air molecules left in the chamber.

This is the most unique vacuum system in the world. When I was told that merely pressing two metals together in this atmosphere would cause them to flow together as one, it was almost too much to believe. But the unique and amazing quality of this equipment lies in the fact that it is the only vacuum machine in the world where a scientist can work with material just as if it were out in the open on the bench before him.

Now, if I should say, "If you can duplicate this machine, you will be rewarded with a million dollars," you would probably scoff at such a thought. For most of us, it would

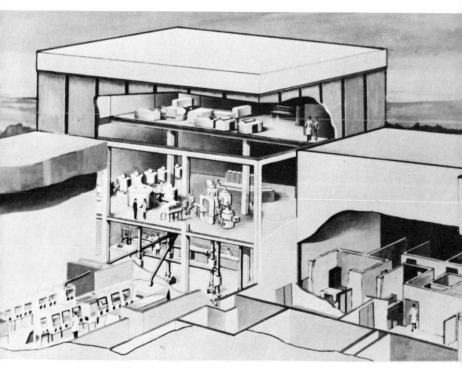

Lunar Receiving Laboratory. Bottom left is biological cabinetry; pipes take gases to upper labs. All works under a vacuum system.

take a college course just to learn how to turn on the switches to get the thing going.

This leads me to an important point. While our mental capabilities in the area of scientific knowledge may be far from on a par with today's scientific "greats," before God all men are equal.

Every Sunday that they are home, Dr. P. R. Bell and a number of other men of science are in the worship service at Seabrook Methodist Church. Here, they are just men among men, and they are the first to admit it. The spiritual truths of God can be understood and received by all men alike. For those truths have attraction to the very depths of man's being. In worship the plumber, the carpenter, the mechanic, the engineer, the secretary, the clerk, the technician, the medical doctor, the bus driver, and the scientist can be captured by the same spiritual truths, and in turn apply them to every need in life.

While we may be unequal in our talents, we can be equal in our commitment. No one has a monopoly on faith, hope, and love. All men are capable of receiving and acting on these life qualities, and anyone who loves God and other people can have faith and hope for every situation.

What Comes Next?

According to Nobel Prize scientist Harold Urey, the scientific community was established at the Manned Spacecraft Center with the coming of Dr. Wilmot Hess.

Dr. Hess, an upstate New Yorker, did undergraduate study at Oberlin, and his graduate work was done at the University of California, Berkeley, where he got his Ph.D. in physics.

In 1954 he worked on the Cyclotron. After spending three years in nuclear weapons development with Edward Teller at Livermore, he returned to the radiation laboratory at Berkeley to work on the Bevatron, the biggest accelerator in the world at that time, in an effort to understand the inside of a nucleus.

In 1959 and 1960 Dr. Hess returned to Livermore to head a group of scientists involved in Project Plowshare (Isaiah 2:4). They studied ways to use nuclear bombs for industrial and non-military applications. Plans were developed for digging an Isthmian Canal, a new Panama Canal, with nuclear bombs. Political and budget problems prevented the job from being carried out, but the plans are laid out and waiting.

In 1961 Goddard Space Flight Center called him to be chief of their Theoretical Division. About a hundred scientists were active in this division. There were astronomers and geochemists, some of whom were dealing with cosmic rays, and others with the celestial mechanics. The Goddard Center was NASA's most scientifically oriented laboratory. Dr. Hess remained there until 1966, when he accepted the position of Director of Science and Applications at the Manned Space Center.

What does a man with these credentials have to do with putting a man on the moon? Very little except in an advisory capacity. He is concerned primarily with what a man does after he gets on the moon. That fact sets the stage for a broader discussion of what is going on at the Manned Spacecraft Center.

Putting a man on the moon has been the national goal of this decade. Technological and engineering people have been the miracle workers in this effort. But what happens after the moon landing? That is the big question. This is the reason for the establishment of a scientific community at the Center. Space technology and engineering will continue beyond their first goal of putting a man on the moon because we now have scientific goals for the space program, calling for more technology and engineering.

In the public's mind no technological feat could be bigger than putting a man on the moon. After all, that is the reason for going there in the first place. In 1960 President Kennedy felt that feat would lift a country's spirit. Now, that goal is being realized—thanks to some superb technology and engineering. And thanks to "Science and Applications," all of our sophisticated hardware will not end in a junk heap following a manned lunar landing.

Compared to the goal of putting a man on the moon, the objectives of the scientific community may not seem especially exciting. However, the act of putting a man on the moon must be implemented with other objectives. So, scientists are involved in establishing these goals.

What are the specific goals of "Science and Applications"? According to Dr. Hess there are three: (1) Bring back lunar samples in the undisturbed state of moon environment—the vacuum. Exposure to earth atmosphere would oxidize the material, changing it into something different from it's original makeup. (2) Place several geophysical instruments, such as a seismometer, on the moon's surface. This equipment can study moon shock waves caused by either space collisions or inner tensions. And the megnetometer will give readings on the effects of the sun's magnetic field on the moon. If the sun's magnetic field penetrates (or fails to penetrate) the moon, scientists can come close to knowing the composition and quality of the surface material. For instance, copper would capture the sun's magnetic field; quartz would let it through. Again if the moon is a good insulator (like quartz), you would have to say that the inside is quite cold, and if the moon is a good conductor, you would conclude the inside is very hot rock. (3) Apply the geologic method. The astronauts are trained to be field geologists. They will be able to look at soil and rock formations and make judgments as to what might have caused them to be the way they are.

Dr. Hess also described some other imaginative projects. One has to do with the possibility of building a large telescope on the moon through which the heavens may be explored without having the distortion effects of an atmosphere. And in the field of photography, the fourteen days of darkness on the moon each month are ideal for long exposures of faint objects. But I am especially excited about the designs that are being drawn for a lunar jeep—a vehicle the astronaut can drive while he is on the moon. In addition to its obvious usefulness, before leaving to return to earth, he could throw a few switches and leave it in remote control, and a group in the NASA Control Center could operate it. A television camera mounted on the front of the jeep would help the controller in guiding the vehicle. He could "drive" it along the surface until he saw an uncommon rock. With the aid of a mechanical scoop, the rock could be picked up and put in a sack. After several such successful stops, the jeep could be parked in a specific place and the sack could be picked up by the astronauts on the next mission.

Dr. Hess added, "We can do this in five years. If you were to ask me what we'll do ten years from now, I'd have to admit

that I have no useful ideas at all. What we should do in ten years depends very much on what we learn on the moon in the next couple of years."

He is saying that *now* he doesn't have the ideas. But as time goes along, he'll have many productive ideas worthy to be considered as goals. Dr. Hess is extremely optimistic about the capabilities of man on the moon.

As a case in point, he says, "People were worried about how well the astronauts in Apollo 7 would be able to move about in zero gravity. And then the operational movies taken inside the capsule reveal they had no trouble at all—they had a great time. Their performance looked like Walt Disney's otters—a true-to-life Walt Disney thing that had otters sliding down slides and things like that. They would get in the sleeping bag, float out of the bag, go around a corner, and glide to the upper deck, etc. Walt Cunningham said, 'I could point to a corner, bounce off a spot, and not miss that corner by two inches.' They would push off one bulkhead and float over to the other side without even thinking. They were having a great time and obviously enjoying it. No one ever thought prior to the flight that they would be able to do that."

After viewing these fantastic movies, I agree that our astronauts will devise a moon method of body navigation. It's interesting to watch them in the 1/6-G simulator at the Center as they try to move about in their "bungee" cord harness with one-sixth of their weight touching the earth. In that simulated moon gravity situation, they have found that the kangaroo hop seems the natural way to "walk." Possibly this will be the best way to get around on the moon.

Now, let's look at our goals again. The technology and engineering goal of getting a man on the moon will be accomplished when man gets there. Next, come the scientific goals. The same scientists and technicians who have created the hardware to get a man on the moon will also develop the hardware that can plant a telescope on the moon's surface, or can put a moon jeep to work, or can do whatever "Science and Applications" feels should be done. Today's dreamers are the realists of the future. They know the folly of attempting to be more specific now, but they are alert and flexible to each opportunity. Dr. Hess referred to a comment made by Ernest Lawrence in a press conference when he was asked about the plans to build the Bevatron, the biggest atomic accelerator of the era. The newsmen asked, "Well, what are you going to discover with that machine?" Lawrence answered, "If I knew that, I wouldn't build it."

As we reflect upon how our manned space program has progressed to its present level, we recognize that one of the big factors in that advancement has been insight and daring of those in charge in the establishment of goals—even though those goals may require modification with changing circumstances. And it seems to me that this approach is practical for every situation in life.

What comes after the moon landing? I don't know. And nobody can be absolutely sure. But we can be certain of this much—we are going somewhere beyond a moon landing. We are on our way to an ultimate goal that has not yet been determined.

PART II

Truth Through Space Pictures

Too Close to See

For many years moon watchers have looked obliquely through telescopes at the left side of the moon and saw what they thought was a semi-circular ridge on that section of the lunar surface. Repeated attempts were made to peek around the outer perimeter of the moon to see what was there. But there was no way of knowing until Lunar Orbiter sailed around to that angle of the moon, set its camera, and clicked this panoramic scene of the Orientale Basin. Whatever the object was—planet or comet—that crashed into the moon, the impact pushed up ridges of lunar material that rippled into their circular positions following the shock waves of the collision. What you see in this picture had never been seen by anyone prior to the Lunar Orbiter's picture-taking in 1966 (and Russia's moon shot a few months earlier).

But, here is a startling fact—for years we have been preoccupied with lunar craters without knowing that there are craters on the earth's surface just as large and impressive as those seen on the moon. We were unaware of this until our space cameras turned their lenses back toward earth.

How is it possible that we have lived on earth all these years without having a full knowledge of the craters? A number of explanations come to mind, including the wearing down

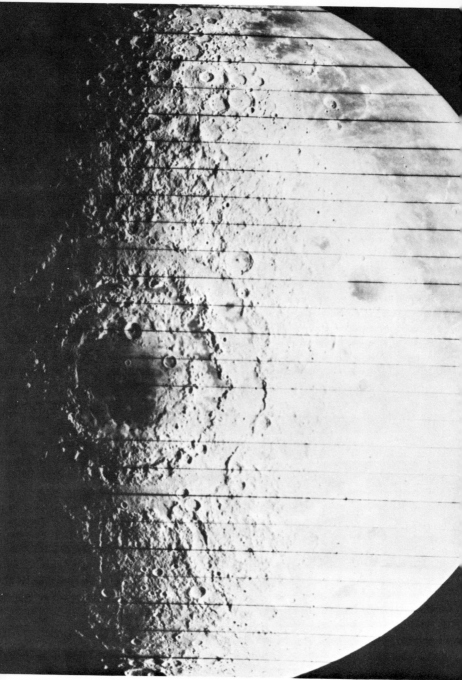

Orientale Basin. Extreme left of the moon. Taken by Lunar IV from an altitude of 1,690 miles. The outer ring is about 600 miles in diameter. The large dark area in the upper right is Oceanus Procellarum.

of the crater rims by water and wind erosion and the camou-flaging effect of wild vegetation and plant life. But, undoubt-edly, the main reason that we have been unaware of the significance of these massive earth craters is that *we are too close to them.* At such close range we have been unable to see what they were, or rather *that* they were. This analogy is certainly true in many other areas of life . . . we tend to lose our perspective because we are so close to a problem or situation that we fail to grasp its full implication and mean-ing.

Here is a good example of what I mean. Our space cameras pictured a number of old established silver mines situated around the edge of a large earth depression in Mexico. Evident-ly, studies of rock samples caused the initial probes in the area which led to a discovery of silver deposits. And now, from space photographs we see that the mines are actually spotted around the outer rim of a crater that is so large no one recognized it for what it was. The big question is—does the presence of silver here bear any relationship to the fact that the crater was scooped out long ago by a cosmic collision? And, if by any chance this relationship does exist, can we assume there may be silver deposits on the rim of other cra-ters?—known and unknown. What other hidden secrets will future space pictures of our earth reveal?

Occasionally, we hear expansive comment about the high cost of our space program—and it does cost a great deal. But, it seems to me that we are just beginning to see the possi-bilities of the tremendous returns from our investment. At this point we know very few of the secrets God may be ready to reveal about this earth of ours. But we are learning more every day. Space exploration tells us more about what is "out there." It is also telling us a great deal about what is "down here"—the location of ore deposits, the habits of marine life, etc.

Yes, the benefits of our space effort are many and varied. There is so much more involved than the physical act of putting a man down on the moon—or beyond. Who knows?

I Thirst

It is a bit startling to realize that sixty percent of the human body is water, but actually, a major part of our total environment is water. A look at our oceans from outer space will convince us of this. As a matter of fact, we couldn't live without water.

Three-quarters of the earth surface is covered by water. And underneath exposed lands are rivers that empty into the underwater valleys in the oceans. It is amazing to realize that these underground rivers are as large as the ones we see cutting wiggles through the earth's crust.

Now we are involved in the exploration of the moon where there is no moisture. In a very real sense we will be like "fish out of water." This poses one of the biggest technological problems that must be overcome. If man is to survive, his watery environment must be taken with him wherever he goes in outer space.

The spaceship itself constitutes a closed life support system for the astronauts. Onboard food consumed by the engine-like body of man, along with inhaled oxygen within the pressurized cabin, work together to produce carbon dioxide, water, and heat. The carbon dioxide in the spacecraft atmosphere is absorbed in Lithium hydroxide canisters; the heat is radiated into space; and with proper management, sweat, respiratory water, and urine can be processed in much the same way that germ-infested city water is processed every day on the earth.

This same type of closed life support system is also present within the spacesuit, giving two complete systems. NASA's top spacesuit authority, Mr. Edward L. Hayes, puts it this way: "We are trying to do in a telephone booth what the Lord did in the world!" And in his typical wit he adds, "You surely can't afford a rip in your britches!"

The presence of that watery creature (man) in his canned atmosphere on the lunar surface means that water has been introduced on the moon for the first time in many, many years—if the river-like wiggles on the lunar surface were indeed rivers. Chemical analysis of lunar soil samples will tell us that story. Water may not be a must for the moon, but it is for the man on the moon.

On earth, in space, on the moon—man thirsts for water, thereby giving the Biblical analogy universal implications. On earth and on the moon, man echoes the cry of the Psalmist, "My soul thirsts for God, for the living God."

The Holy Land

Throughout history men have attempted to map the Bible lands with the best instruments available at the time. However, these maps are poor substitutes for the true shape of the lands. Hardly any two agree in their dimensions.

But, at last, the click of an astronaut's camera has given us a precise map of the entire region. The pictures tell it like it is—and in color, too. A sketchy drawing from inaccurate figures does little to stir imaginations, but this picture literally puts us on top of things.

From this perspective we get God's "view," not in the sense that God is "up there," any more than He is "down here," "in there," or anywhere, but in the sense that He chose one special part of earth to be the stage of man's historical beginnings.

Never before in human history had man been able to scan at a glance this vast bit of historic real estate. Oh, we've been able to see bits and pieces of it, but it took a camera mounted in an orbiting spacecraft to give us a full and accurate perspective.

Here is where it all happened: powerful Joseph in Egypt west of the Nile in the fertile river valley; Joseph and Mary with the infant Jesus in self-imposed Egyptian exile; Moses

The Holy Land, viewed from Egypt and across Sinai. Taken from Gemini 11.

spending forty years in the Sinai wilderness east of the Nile River looking after the sheep; the judges; the kings; the foreign rulers—all were here. We can readily identify the land of the Philistines, the Mediterranean Sea where Paul traveled so extensively and was shipwrecked, the Dead Sea, and the Jordan River.

It is a fascinating exercise to recall a particular Biblical story, look at this picture, and "see" it happen all over again.

It all opens up right before your eyes—the beloved stories take on greater meaning as we are able to identify their locale on the encompassing space photo of where it all happened.

Life on the Moon

When that stone, nineteen yards in diameter, rolled 250 yards across the moon's surface, did it run over an ant? This question sounds like something out of the comic strip "B.C."

It poses a question that is frequently asked at the Manned Spacecraft Center: Is there any form of life on the moon? The general attitude among the scientists is, "We don't think so, but we are open to the possibility, and we are preparing for the eventuality that there may be life forms on the moon."

The scientist's openness toward the possibility of lunar life forms can be illustrated by the elaborate preparations made at the Lunar Receiving Laboratory—the reception point for everything and everyone returning from the moon. Every conceivable precaution is being made to keep down the slightest contamination of our earth by moon bacteria. If such microscopic life is discovered, the lunar bacteria will be exposed to sterile animals, previously unexposed to germs of any kind. If the animals can handle the moon bacteria, then we will assume a man can do as well.

Meanwhile, scientists and doctors will observe the astronauts to see if any moon virus is affecting them, and botanists will test what, if anything, moon bacteria might do to our plant life. Fish and game will be exposed to any miscroscopic life. What does it all mean? Simply this: When the returning

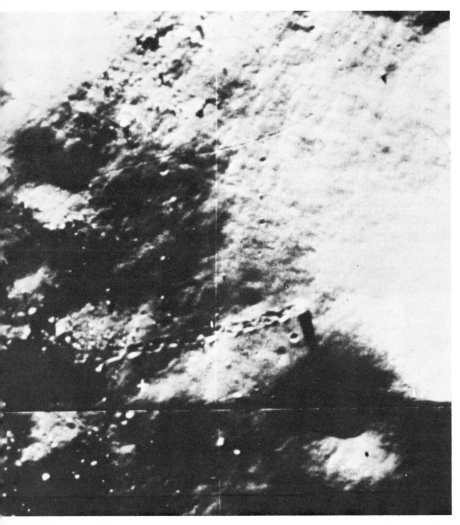

A dislodged rock, nineteen yards in diameter, in the crater Vitello has left a 250 yard trail on the lunar surface after rolling down a slope into a depression. Picture taken by Lunar Orbiter V.

lunar astronauts and the scientists and doctors exposed to them leave the Receiving Laboratory after their quarantine period, they will have a clean bill of health. There will be no danger of any form of contamination.

From all of this elaborate preparation and precaution, I would say that the NASA scientists take rather seriously the possibility of life forms on the moon. Admittedly, "life forms" in the lunar scientist's thinking means miscroscopic bacteria. But I am still biased toward the ant idea!

This openness toward any eventuality is a posture of truth in any situation, whether in a housewife or a scientist. An open mind learns, lives, and loves. And that is Truth.

Look at the Earth

This is the way earth would look to you from the moon. It would appear eighty times as bright as the moon looks to us. Upon seeing it for the first time, a likely exclamation might be, "Heavens above, look at that!"

And our earth would be part of the "heavens above."

Actually, our earth *is* a part of those heavens. This fact should reassure those who have trouble bringing God "down to earth" from the lofty reaches of the heavens. But, since God dwells in the heavens and our earth is a part of those heavens, He is present on earth as well.

However, if we have been prone to think of God as being only on earth, this view from the moon should enlarge our concept of Him. Possibly, we've thought of Him as being on earth simply because we are. But, He is there with the astronauts on the moon too.

Seeing the earth from the moon as you see it here, and seeing that it is indeed a part of the universal heavens, should increase our awareness of God.

God is as big as the infinite stretches of space—He's here; He's there; He's everywhere.

Earth coming over the moon's horizon. Taken from Apollo 8 by Astronauts Borman, Lovell, and Anders.

A Closer Look

An honest attitude toward any scientific endeavor should be: "We just want to see what God has done." It doesn't seem to me that this is a controversial idea for an inquiring mind.

Throughout history the moon has held a mysterious fascination for the human race. The only difference between our approach today and that of the past is that we are determined to get a closer view of it.

I don't believe that God intends for us to be limited in our view and perspective of the moon. Just a short time ago our approach was limited to what our airplane pilots could observe from twelve miles above the earth. And then our perspective enlarged as astronauts viewed the moon from earth orbit, a few hundred miles out in space. Next, Apollo 8 gave us a closer look, when for the first time men actually orbited the moon and viewed it from close range.

Successive lunar missions take us closer and closer, and it won't be long until man's moving about on the moon's surface is commonplace. The curious drive that demands "a closer look" is God-given. It is a part of our human heritage. We are impelled to "move ever closer" in our search for Truth, and in doing so we move progressively closer to our divine destiny.

A bright ray crater around the back side of the moon. Taken from Apollo 8 by Astronauts Borman, Lovell, and Anders.

Now

This picture recalls to mind the words of the Psalmist, "For a thousand years in thy sight are but as yesterday when it is past . . ." (Psalm 90:4).

While the Bible is not a book of science, its truths certainly apply to science. In this case we see it apply to space science. From the point where this picture was made on the other side of the moon, our earth looks far, far away. How easy from this vantage point to come to an understanding of the eternal nature of God!

Routine earth questions like, "What time shall we get up in the morning?" wouldn't make sense in lunar orbit. Sunrise and sunsets come so rapidly. Clock time isn't necessarily God's time. Clock events, whether those events are the movements of little hands on a clock or the earth turning away from the sun bringing on darkness or light, are the means man uses to organize his earthly life.

If a man really wanted to get a "feel" for God's eternity, he could certainly run an interesting experiment in his spaceship. All he would have to do while floating in space is turn off his radio contact with the earth, pull a shade over the small window, and let his wrist watch run down. In just a little while he wouldn't know whether he was coming or going or how long he had been asleep or awake. All he would feel is one big NOW. And that is eternity. No beginning, no ending, just NOW.

Perhaps this new awareness would enable us to better understand why Jesus Christ said, "*Now*, is the day of salvation." He didn't say, "Tomorrow," or at "12:00 noon." Jesus did not use any clock-time reference. He was talking in terms of eternity. For that was His nature, and that is God's nature.

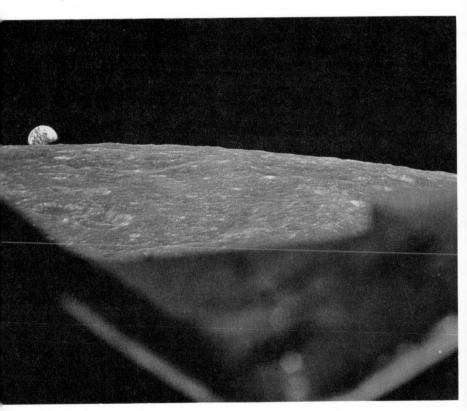

Space Talk

There was a time in history when man visualized a three-storied universe. Heaven was "up there" with the stars, planets, and moons. Earth was "here," and hell was "down there" under the crust of the earth.

If a person has trouble rejecting the three-storied concept of the universe, one look at the picture of the earth from the moon, will cause him to "forget it!" When an astronaut stands on the moon, the three-storied idea certainly breaks down. "Up there" could point to the earth, and we earthlings know that this earth is no heaven, even if we do get an occasional heavenly glimpse. On the moon, "here" would refer to the lunar surface. And "down there" would be under the lunar crust.

While space pictures shatter this concept of a three-storied universe, spatial words and expressions are in vogue as much as ever before. This may be hard for some thinkers to understand because of their conviction that such spatial terms are incompatible with the sun-centered concept of the universe. However, the sun-centered concept of the universe is outdated to the modern astronomer. Actually, the latest thinking points to the idea that we are part of a solar system located on the outer edge of one of many galaxies.

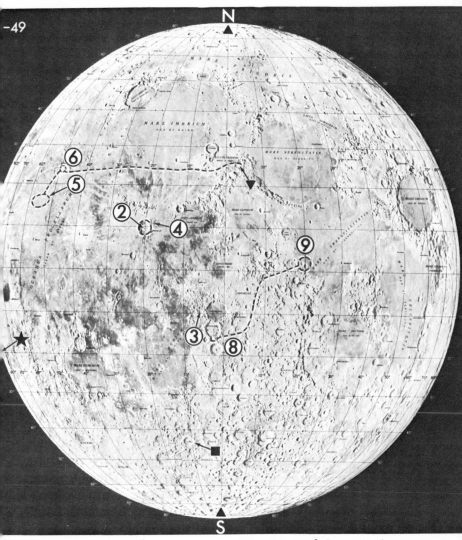

Moon Map. *The numbers are constant formations used for navigation toward proposed landing sites.*

  2. *Copernicus*

  3-9. *Ridge-like effect.*

  4. *Mountains on NNE rim of Copernicus.*

  5. *Flat Plateau area.*

  6. *West of Aristarchus.*

  8. *Arzachel (the Southernmost of 3 craters).*

  9. *Two small craters*

■ *Tycho*

▼ *Apennines Mountains on the edge of the "Marsh of Decay."*

83

No matter which planet you might be standing on, the words "up" and "down" are always applicable to *your* position. These spatial terms are not only admissable; they are absolutely necessary to carry on conversations anywhere. For example, the use of these terms does not do away with the "in" word of modern social sciences where everything is "deep"—*depth* psychology, *depth* psychiatry, *depth* philosophy, *depth* theology. The word *depth* is a spatial word that should be added to other spatial terms and used whenever it can transmit meaning.

When the astronaut is in orbit, he may say, "Everything is looking up." The spatial term "up" in this sense means everything is A-Okay. Whenever a space shot slides, astronauts have been known to be *down*cast. That usage is self-explanatory.

When I looked at the large wall map of the moon's surface at NASA and saw "north," "south," "east," "west," and listened to the scientist explain that "you have to go 'up' from Mare Tranquillitaties to get to Mare Serenitatis," and that " 'down' here below Oceanus Procellorum is Mare Humorum," it became eminently clear that lunar scientists are unashamed to use spatial terms when they are needed for descriptive clarity. We would do well to stay in step and not attempt to appear more sophisticated and scientific than the scientists.

No matter how you view the universe, it looks like such spatial words as "up" and "down" are applicable in this age of space. They are used by space scientists, engineers, and technicians as well as by the man on the street. And if we are to communicate the good news of the Christian faith in modern terms, we must use these "modern" words, but that does not mean we believe we are living in a three-storied universe. It simply means that we want to communicate, and these are good words to use because most people understand them.

Modern man still looks "up" to God. And nobody wants to spend eternity "down" there.

More Than Likely

A young earth crater is pictured on the next page. It is one among many. The earth is pocked with craters, but unlike on the moon, they are not usually defined clearly. The winds and the rains have all but erased their identity.

It is possible that a study of the earth craters will help us to understand the origins of those on the moon. And study we must—because as of now we know very little about many of these earth craters. For instance, in the case of the Mauritania's Richat structure, all we can say now is that possibly it was caused from the erosion of a volcanic plug or intrusion.

It could well be that even after we have landed on the moon we can only guess as to what caused certain conditions. But this should present no problem—so often our "factual" assertions are simply possibilities. To illustrate: we agree to the possibility that Columbus might not have discovered America first, and it is possible that the Wright Brothers did not fly the first airplane.

So, it is likely that on the moon we will have to settle for mere possibilities for a time. When more scientists say, "Now, more than likely this happened by . . ." we can then begin to feel we know something. For after all, isn't this the state of most discoveries? "It's more than likely . . ."

85

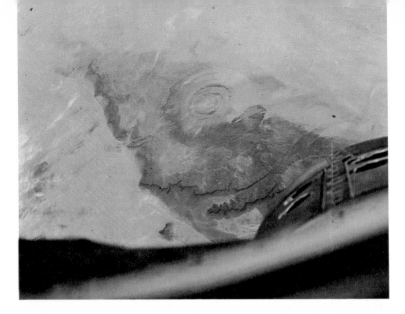

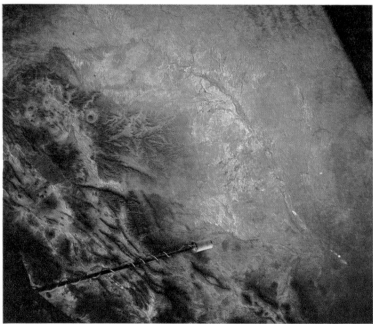

(Upper) The Richat structure in Mauritania. Taken from Gemini 4 by Astronauts McDivitt and White. (Lower) Volcanic craters and igneous intrusions in Texas and Mexico. Taken from Gemini 12 by Astronauts Lovell and Aldrin.

The Blackness of Space

If you stand outside on a crisp, clear day and look up, you will see bright, blue sky. "Blue skies, nothing but blue skies." However, when you go far out into space, the blue disappears into blackness. And if you stand on the moon and look "up" at the earth, you would be looking into "the wild black yonder," and through that blackness, you would see a milky white and bluish earth.

This is one of the great discoveries of space travel. Blue is a light reflection of our earth's atmosphere. Therefore, when we leave this atmosphere, there is blackness. On the other hand, when an object with the capability to reflect light whizzes though space, it "lights up." It was interesting that on the Apollo 7 mission the astronauts confused water droplets from their spacecraft's dumping system with stars! The reflection was so intense.

Yes, it's dark up there, but when the astronaut's eyes adjust to that darkness, it fades into semi-darkness. For out in the nothingness of space, the heavens come alive with little lights —some dim and some very bright. As one scientist commented, "It's nothingness crammed with a lot of little bright lights." What a sight that must be!

Yet, without the stars, planets, and moons out in space,

there would be only a black nothingness. Indeed, space pictures make it easier to understand that out of nothing all things were created. They reveal dramatically the Biblical truth —out of nothing, God created the universe.

It must be a beautiful sight—to look down from outer space toward the earth. But I continue to be thrilled by our view of outer space from the earth. . . it's so soft and blue. Somehow, I think I like it better from here . . . I don't like the dark or black nothingness. I don't like nothingness. That's where I came from, and I don't want to go back "there."

I See the Moon and the Moon Sees Me

The picture of the moon over the Pacific Ocean, shown on the next page seems to cause a common reaction among those who view it. Could the earth be more peaceful than this as it literally turns the brightness of the moon up by its own rotation? During each twenty-four hour period, first one-half the world and then the other goes to sleep in the darkness dotted by flicks of star lights and the soft glow of the moon. This seems to be nature's way of saying to the sensitive soul, "Go to sleep now. I'll keep one eye open—or half open—all is well."

But what else is happening in nature? For one thing, earth's seas are feeling the tug of the moon's gravity. At times the tides in Galveston Bay, only a few blocks from Seabrook Methodist Church, rise as much as five feet. When this happens, that peaceful looking moon plays havoc with the bulkheads of the beach homes. Usually they take the pounding very well, but their occupants feel a great sense of relief when the moon journeys around to the earth's other side, leaving behind a low tide for a time.

The pull of the moon on the earth, however, is nothing compared to the impact of earth's gravity on the moon. As the moon pulls the tide up onto our beaches, the earth literally pulls the moon into a bulging shape toward earth. Earth's

Looking at the moon over the Pacific horizon. Taken over the Pacific Ocean from Gemini 7 by Astronauts Borman and Lovell. They later orbited the moon.

gravatational pull is six times that of the moon—giving earth the edge in this battle of the bulges.

Which of these views of the moon is correct? Both are right. It's all in how you look at it. The scientific view sees the interaction of the physical laws of the two heavenly bodies, and it provides a warning of any great danger to the one by the other. The findings of the scientists can help protect man on either planet.

But the romantic view of the poet is just as authentic as the revealing view of the scientist. The poet's interpretation of the moon stirs the soul of man and triggers aesthetics in his spirit. In the shadowy face of the moon he sees beauty, peace, serenity, romance, purity—and he meditates on the things of God.

Through both of these attitudes and interpretations we come to know the truth. But these remain mere half-truths if they do not lead us to their source—the Creator of the heavens and the earth and the Revealer of all Truth everywhere.

Surveyor III

On April 17, 1967, a rocket blasted off from earth with a machine that made a soft landing on the moon two days later. That mechanical creature took pictures of the lunar surface, of the earth, of the sun, and of itself digging in the moon crust. The craft's mechanical shovel scooped up the lunar soil, laid it on one of the landing gear pads in plain view of the camera which photographed the granular earth-like soil, and then a transmitter sent the picture back to earth!

That little digging machine up there on the moon is typical of man's habits of discovery. He has been a "digger" throughout all of history. But man's great efforts on earth, whether for oil in the ocean or diamonds in Africa, cannot equal the accomplishment of that little bucket on Surveyor III that drove a few inches into the lunar surface and ploughed a ditch 24 inches long. Up to this time, that is the most complex digging operation in man's history.

But a man standing on the lunar surface with a spoon in his hand would make Surveyor III seem very crude. The successful lunar landing and operation of this digging apparatus is one of man's finest technological accomplishments, but it cannot be compared to the crowning achievement of man standing on the moon himself and doing his own digging.

Until this is accomplished in a practical and continuing pattern, man's restless nature remains uneasy and unsatisfied.

When a man actually stands beside Surveyor III, the thoughtful observer will reflect on the truth that our best mechanical machine cannot be compared to the human machine that God made. A review of our space accomplishments prompts most of us to exclaim, "Look what we've done!" And it will be the truth. But even a greater truth is, "Look what God has done in creating a man who is able to do that."

It is God who has made our noblest accomplishments possible in the first place. By putting the mysteries out there and giving us the knowledge to solve a few, He remains in charge of the universe.

An Eclipse

Because of the brightness around the outer circle in this picture, you would probably guess that this is an eclipse of the sun. It is. However, this particular eclipse is not caused by the moon coming between the earth and the sun. Look again. What you actually see here is an eclipse as viewed from the moon—the earth is eclipsing the sun. This startling picture was snapped from Surveyor III at just the right moment to catch this amazing phenomenon.

It doesn't stretch the imagination too much to catch several analogies of truth from this picture. We (earth) can put out another person's light (moon) by casting a shadow of gloom; we (earth) look entirely different from another person's (moon) view; we (earth) can block out the light of God (sun) from others (moon), and yet the light of God (sun) is never completely put out—there's always enough left to know that He's here.

In addition to these, there is a profound truth that we can see through the events that made possible this unique photograph. While the earth was rotating around the sun, the moon was rotating around the earth. At the precise moment that the Surveyor III camera snapped this shot, sun, earth, and

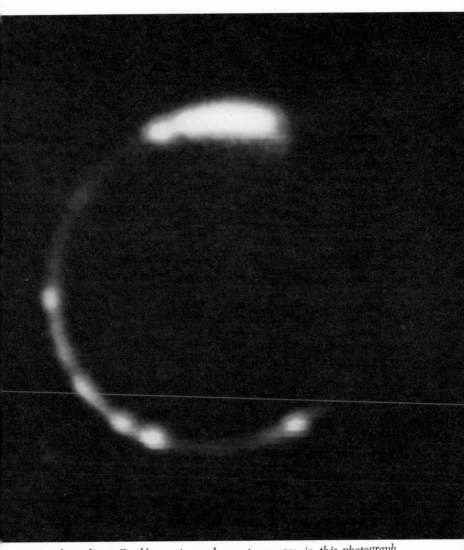

A solar eclipse. Earth's sunrise and sunset are seen in this photograph of the earth's disc passing across the sun. Photographed from a vantage point on the moon by a Surveyor III TV camera.

moon were lined up neatly—three dots on an imaginary line. What a tragedy it is that we become so engrossed in a mere existence balanced between darkness and light that we are oblivious to the movement of the heavenly bodies responsible for it. When we really ponder the decision required to get the sun and earth and moon in this position, we come to an awareness that a perfect Creator did it all!

The idea of a static God just doesn't make sense. The movements of these heavenly bodies, the gravitational influence of each on the other, the bombardment of the planets by cosmic rays and meteoritic space waste, plus uncounted other influences of chemical change—all point to one fact: God did not at some specific time in the past create the heavens and earth and then stop. He still creates through all of the forces of nature.

The acceptance of this truth lays the foundation for the philosophical question: How long will God go on with this creation before He's finished? Immediately after posing the question, we are aware of the haunting idea that if He ever did complete creation, we would be finished.

And the more you think about it all, the more the fact of immortality makes sense. If we die before becoming a finished product of creation, and that is inevitable for us from the physical standpoint, then somehow, somewhere, by somebody there must be an end to all this wear and tear. We become a new creation, the ultimate creation of our eternal God and Father. But for now we are like these planets. We must continue moving on. God is still creating, and we are part of that creation and of that creating process.

The Island

By looking closely at 'the "Island" picture you will see a formation that looks very much like an island formed by two dry river beds.

This picture of the moon was taken by Lunar Orbiter IV. A great deal of controversy and conjecture has developed as lunar scientists have attempted to understand what caused these strange formations. But there will be no answers short of a chemical analysis of soil samples. These will reveal whether or not there is any water history on the moon.

Some would scoff at the idea of water ever being on the lunar surface. But we must not laugh too soon. Remember that the highest mountain peaks on earth have fossil deposits of sea creatures left there many years ago by water masses. Is it any harder to believe that water was once on the moon than it is to believe that our country's tallest mountains were once submerged under water?

The way these beds flow out onto and disperse into a lower level seems to indicate that a liquid movement caused the erosion. If water did not form these "river" beds, what did? At present there are various theories but no concrete answers.

Becoming absorbed in moon pictures like these can be an exciting adventure. We cannot identify with the scientists

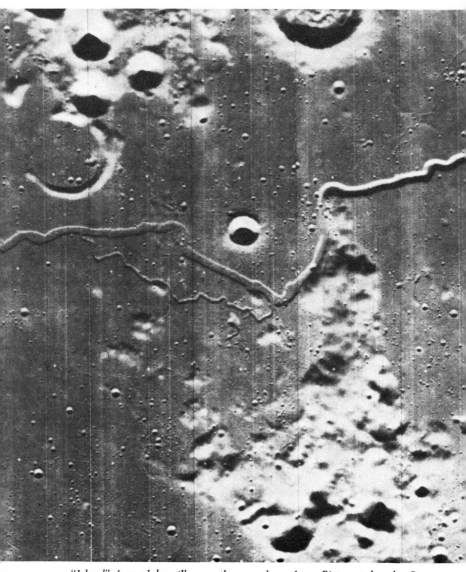

"Island" formed by rilles on the moon's surface. Picture taken by Lunar Orbiter IV.

who are to be privileged to work with lunar samples. We share in their curiosity, and we want to know how "river" beds were formed on the moon. We learn to identify with the scientist in sharing his excitment and enthusiasm.

On a clear night go outside and look up at the full moon. Direct your attention to the extreme northwestern area and in your imagination *take off* for that part of the moon. At a distance from the moon of about sixty miles you will have a view identical to what you see in this picture, an island comparable in size to Galveston Island in Texas. Now that you have seen it first hand it has become a part of your own personal experience, but you are still unable to define the origin of what you see. What can you do about it? Nothing, except support the astronauts and scientists who are searching for the answers.

Any person who looks at this "river" bed picture and becomes curious enough to question why it is there and where it came from shares a common experience with the NASA scientists. They welcome our interest and are anxious to share both their questions and their answers with us.

The fact that this book was written at the suggestion of several scientists within the NASA community is ample evidence of the very human side of these men. Only the future will reveal the extent of what they can and will discover with our support. All are curious; some devote time; others money; others sympathy; but we all gain with each discovery.

Seeing Red

The picture you see here was taken with infrared film. Living chlorophyl reflects infrared light, a light of long wavelength. The sensitive film captures the infrared reflections from living plants by registering red. This particular film bypasses the green color and penetrates deeper into the life of the plant itself—to its chemistry of chlorophyl. It gets to the essence of the plant, not by viewing what is green but what is living.

You can share in some of the knowledge gained from these pictures of large land masses. If nothing red shows up on the film, there's no plant life on that part of the earth. Absence of red among forests reveals diseased and dead trees.

What these space pictures of the living chemistry of plants mean for farming and forest industries cannot be put into terms that do justice to the ultimate good accomplished. The cause of conservation has been served in a way that the generations before us never dreamed possible. Certainly, the amazing benefits in space fascinates the inquisitive mind. It is even possible that it will assist in determining locations for drilling water wells in countries where water is more precious than oil.

From the military standpoint, there are many possibilities.

Synthetically camouflaged areas are readily exposed. While the pictured area shows up green, the absence of plant life is obvious because no chlorophyl is present. Then, too, the infrared film defines clearly the farming areas in contrast to the cities and industrial complexes. Dense forests where an enemy might hide can be readily identified and defoliated if necessary.

This is a sobering irony. Films that actually take pictures of life can be used in the killing of that life. So many good things in God's creation can be used for evil. A rock can be used for road beds or for killing a neighbor. Water can save life or destroy it through drowning. Infrared film can help conserve life or it is an aid in killing it.

Our problem is not with rocks, water, or infrared film, but with the man who uses them. What are we going to do with him?

Let's face it. Man without God is his own greatest enemy. Until he learns to live with himself and his Creator there is no predicting what he will do with the countless life-giving or death-dealing provisions supplied by God and intended for man's good.

The Pinacates Volcanic Field

In Spanish the word "pinacates" is the name of a desert beetle. We don't know exactly what caused that name to be given to the land area pictured here. But it is possible from this picture to detect a land mass the shape of a huge beetle —possibly this accounts for the fact that this particular volcanic field is called "pinacates."

NASA selected this land area for serious study and use because it simulates the lunar surface. Astronauts use it as a training ground and make a careful study of the native rock samples. Having a background of knowledge of the various rock formations will enable them to classify various lunar rocks.

One common type of rock formation present on earth is the sedimentary rock, caused by sediments brought together by water. If such formations are found on the moon, it will immediately open up the question as to the source of the water.

While the sedimentary rock may not be common to both the earth and the moon, one type probably is—the lava rock. This is one reason the Pinacates Volcanic Field—a lava field —has been chosen as a simulation area. And space pictures do indicate possible lava flows on the moon.

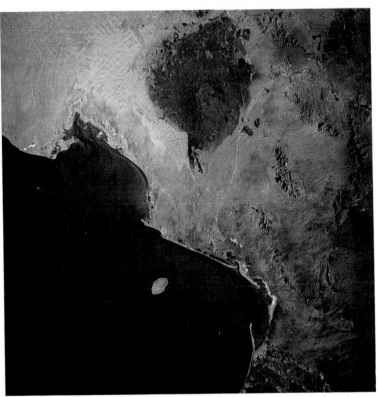

The Pinacates Volcanic Field in Mexico's Sonora Desert. Taken by an unmanned automatic camera from Apollo 6.

Walking around the Pinacates surface in his bulky spacesuit gives the astronaut the feeling that he is actually on the moon. That is, his mind receives signals that tell him he is there, but he also knows that the moon gravity is one-sixth of our earth's gravity. With the same muscle movement on the moon his steps would be six yards long, and if he was untrained in those lesser gravity conditions, he would probably fall flat on his face.

But our simulation engineers have a way of strapping the astronaut in a harness suspended by "bungee" cords. These stretching cords permit only one-sixth of the astronaut's weight to touch the earth, thereby simulating to some extent a moon gravity situation. However, on the moon there is no strap to help keep him upright, so losing one's balance remains a threat.

Then again, in a simulated environment there's no way to measure accurately how high above the lunar surface the astronaut's body will lift each time he strikes the surface with a hammer. To say the least, this could be a most frustrating experience. A blow of the hammer could propel the astronaut into the "air" rather than break a rock loose.

These moon simulations can go just so far, leaving much to be desired. But we must remember that if we knew exactly how to set up moon conditions on earth, there would be no need to go to the moon. One reason for going is to discover just what it is like. No substitute for the real thing is ever acceptable.

I think it is important at this point to introduce a new idea—actually, lunar landings, as important as these are, can be considered interim goals pointing to an even more exciting future. From what we have to go on, the moon's surface may be a better place than earth to simulate a Mars landing. I can just see our astronauts now—roaming the lunar surface in search of another "Pinacates Volcanic Field" to play around with before setting foot on the real thing. If I know these space scientists, they've already got a place picked out on the moon that looks like Mars.

They are always a dozen steps in front of most of us—always looking and planning ahead. It is the quest for, not the capture of, knowledge that sparks enthusiasm.

The Land of Diamonds

If we had a hand in creating the earth, I wonder if we would have done it the way God did. Would we bury beautiful, sparkling, priceless diamonds under hot sand dunes in such a barren, unpopulated, hard-to-reach region of the earth —a place that is very hard to reach from the north or west because of the strong wind and water currents. The picture on the next page of the African Coast and the Namib Desert shows a desolate expanse of sand dunes and basalt deposits. But in past ages, diamond deposits, eroded away from their original mass, were carried by sand and water currents until they were washed inland and came to rest under shifting sands. It looks as if God purposely put diamonds in a place where man would have to go all out to find them.

No, we probably wouldn't do it this way at all. Our tendency would be to put things together in a way that would make it easy on ourselves. Instead of burying anything as precious as diamonds deep in the ground, we would have scattered them out in the open—in obvious places.

Could this be one reason why God puts the highest values of life just beyond arm's reach?—just far enough out in front to make us struggle and strive and if need be, die, to reach the goal? It seems to me this must be the case because we've

The Namib Desert in Southwest Africa. Picture taken from Gemini 5 by Astronauts Cooper and Conrad.

learned the hard way that things which come easy in life are not as satisfying as those things which come through struggle.

Diamonds are valuable because they are hard to find and difficult to process. And the Creator made it this way. Look at the implication of this fact of God's creation. The longer and harder you have to struggle in life toward a goal, the greater your appreciation for that goal when it is attained. The personal rewards for achievement are high because we have so much of ourselves invested in the work that produced it.

To the casual observer this is just a picture of a hot and dry wasteland, but to anyone who had the good fortune to find a diamond, it would look entirely different. For him it would be God-blessed!

Our work gives value to the goal; the achieved goal makes the work worthwhile; and the rough obstacles overcome to reach the goal are soon forgotten in the flush of achievement. That's what the picture says to me. It is a challenge to achieve without regard to the cost.

Seein' Is Believin'

We hear much about air pollution these days. Here on the Gulf Coast they say it has "body" to it! This has become a world-wide problem. Scientists, in measuring the gases of our atmosphere, tell us that the carbon dioxide percentage is increasing rapidly. As you know, carbon dioxide is the gas that comes out of a car exhaust, and it can kill you. Could it be that man could unconsciously poison himself? In wars we gas the enemy; in peace we gas everybody, including ourselves.

As disturbing as this is, too few people seem to take it seriously. We are concerned over isolated pockets of poverty, people's right to dissent, the established order—all of which are relevant areas of concern. But why can't we see that breathing air pollution is an important issue too? It could lead to extinction of the human race.

Until now, our indifference may have been because we couldn't "see" the problem, but space photography has taken care of that. Now we can see the problem right before our eyes. If seein' is believin', we should become great believers after looking at these pictures. Here is the proof: What we need now is to have faith to know that we can solve the prob-

Upper photo. Smog along the Gulf Coast. Taken from Gemini 11.
Lower photo. Los Angeles Smog. Taken from Apollo 7.

111

lem—a faith that will inspire us to positive and creative action.

One of the great truths of life is that faith and sight work smoothly together. Faith will take you through circumstances that you cannot "see" through.

People who live by faith can actually see how God works in their lives. It isn't always possible to see this at any given moment, but, viewed in the perspective of time, we can see how God uses "good" times and "bad" times to bring about His will for our lives.

"Seein' is believin'," whether it pertains to daily personal encounters or air pollution. But the person who believes in truth and is open to truth, "sees more." And hopefully he will do something about what he sees.

PART III

Truth Through Personal Experiences

The Fantastic Voyage
Splashdown
Lord, Guard and Guide the Men Who Fly
The Space-Walker
And Problems Too
Modern Communications
NASA Prayer Breakfast

The Fantastic Voyage

Countdown here at Cape Kennedy is going on now. From the looks of things, I'm more nervous than the Apollo 8 astronauts. They are far more accustomed to actual space travel than I am to watching it take place.

Everything here at Moonport, U.S.A., seems so immense. The space vehicle is a 363 foot stack with a base that would cover a two lane highway. This stack was assembled in the world's largest building, and inside that building is the world's biggest work tower. A kingsized, 131 foot-long "moving van" that moves on four-tracked crawlers transports the rocket from the assembly building to the enormous launch pad. Each track on the crawler weighs one ton. The crawlerway for this transporter is about as wide as an eight lane super-highway. The bigness of the entire complex is overwhelming.

The launch itself is a jaw-dropping experience. Bathed in floodlights, Apollo 8 atop Saturn V stands in the early morning darkness like a gleaming giant popsicle with its cold breath fogging. It seems to fill the sky. From 30 seconds-and-counting until ignition, everything happens so fast that you want to say, "Wait a minute; I'm not set for it!" But the seconds tick off. There is no stopping. And then, "Ignition!" Flames lap out all sides at a distance longer than the entire

116

rocket assembly. At the viewing stand three miles away you see the flames before you hear the blastoff. By the time the sound reaches you, it is a lift-off. The noise can be compared to the blasting sound of an engine equal in horsepower to 1200 miles of cars, bumper to bumper, with their engines revved up.

Saturn V starts upward so slowly that it takes ten seconds to clear the tower that stands beside the rocket. As it rises gently from the pad, gaining speed ever so quickly, earth-shaking blasts of shock waves press hard on you. These fast-hitting popping explosions are felt as much as heard. Up, up, up she goes. As the rocket soars, it trails a span of fire that burns a hot silver white against the ocean of blue sky. At thirty-five miles from liftoff the first stage drops off and the second stage fires amidst a great billow of smoke. It is a gripping experience that triggers spontaneous applause from the spectators. A person there without goose bumps is a person without nerve endings. You tremble with the earth as it moves beneath you. It is a magnificent anxiety!

After one and one-half earth orbits, Apollo 8 was cleared to "go for the moon." These men were really on their way. Three days later, they fired the big service module engine that placed them in parking orbit around the moon. Jim Lovell says that they never saw the moon as they approached lunar orbit because in pointing the service module engine toward the moon, they were facing the earth. He said, "We took it in faith that the moon would be there." Shortly after braking into lunar orbit, they looked out the windows, and there was the moon. They were actually within sixty miles of the lunar surface. And we were right there with them with the help of their television camera.

The bigness of the launch complex and the physical impressions of the launch itself were so overpowering that words cannot describe it, But something happened Christmas Eve that dwarfed the mammoth launch complex, the launch, and the lunar orbit itself. Man's spirit and our Creator's Spirit met in what was the first worship service from "outside the world." Astronauts Anders, Lovell, and Borman read from the Holy Bible as they orbited the moon.

Anders read: "In the beginning, God created the heaven and the earth. And the earth was without form and void and darkness was upon the face of the deep. And the spirit of God moved upon the face of the waters. And God said, Let there be light: and there was light. And God saw the light, that it was good: and God divided the light from the darkness."

The Good Book was passed to Lovell, and in a commanding resonance he read: "And God called the light Day, and the darkness he called Night. And the evening and the morning were the first day. And God said, Let there be a firmament in the midst of the waters, and let it divide the waters from the waters. And God made the firmament, and divided the waters which were under the firmament from the waters which were above the firmament: and it was so. And God called the firmament Heaven. And the evening and morning were the second day."

And then Borman concluded: "And God said, Let the waters under the heaven be gathered together unto one place, and let the dry land appear: and it was so. And God called the dry land Earth; and the gathering together of the waters called he Seas: And God saw that it was good—And from the crew of Apollo 8, we pause with good night, good luck, a Merry Christmas and God bless all of you—all of you on the good earth."

To which Apollo Control replied: "This is Apollo Control, Houston. The speakers in the order that they read from what we believe to be chapters from Genesis were Bill Anders, Jim Lovell, and Frank Borman. That's both a Biblical and a geological lesson that none of us will forget. At 86 hours and 9 minutes into the flight, this is Apollo Control, Houston."

Of all that took place on the Apollo 8 mission, this Christmas Eve worship service from lunar orbit was by far the biggest, most impressionable, dramatic single event. Two thousand years ago wise men saw a star that stirred worship in their souls. Using a star as a navigational aid they found the

118

babe, Jesus Christ, who was Truth in the flesh. On the eve of the celebration of the birth of that same Jesus, three astronauts orbiting the moon looked down upon that heavenly body and worship was stirred within their souls. In both historical instances God used the magnificence of the heavens to stir adoration in the souls of man.

If we ever doubted that our Creator was a part of our space travels, we should doubt no longer. Not only is He a part of it, He is a partner. The Christmas Eve worship service from space is evidence of that fact.

Some have speculated what Jesus Christ's reactions might be if He were born into this space age instead of into His pre-scientific age. It is an illegitimate speculation because Christ is born into every age where men are open to universal truths.

On that memorable night of the Apollo 8 mission He was born again in the souls of three astronauts, and listeners everywhere were deeply moved. This was the biggest event on the fantastic voyage.

Splashdown

When the Apollo 7 astronauts were safe in orbit, we experienced a great sense of relief. But being captured in orbit hardly fits our earth picture of safety. The men were alive, and for the most part, in good humor. But they were not home.

Their return home began as they splashed down in the Atlantic Ocean. However, for one astronaut's wife, family, and friends it really began when someone from outside the house shouted that the craft was clearly visible going over Houston on its final pass. Shortly thereafter the voice of Paul Haney at Mission Control came over the special squawk box installation and captured everybody's attention. In a few moments we turned on the television set and searched the overcast sky for the billowy parachutes with their precious cargo.

When the time for splashdown came and there was no contact established with the craft, the anxiety was intense. It must be very near by, but there was no voice, no beacon . . . nothing. What happened?

The cone shaped vehicle had flipped apex down with the astronauts inside hanging face down, and communication was impossible. The men's egress training in the Gulf of Mexico for just this possibility paid off. A button was punched, inflated plastic bags popped the craft rightside up, and in a short time, they were hoisted into a helicopter for a quick transfer to the aircraft carrier Essex.

As one astronaut's wife said, "It was the best part of the flight." The men were safe and almost home.

Our astronauts keep reminding us that the mission is to go to the moon—and return! We are earthmen traveling in space, but no matter how far we go, there is always that innate desire to return. There is adventure in our conquest of outer space, but there's no place like home.

This then is what every splashdown teaches. Without the splashdown all preceding adventures turn into nightmares. Our trips to the moon and beyond are not ultimately taking us away from the earth—they simply provide lively situations that make coming home the highlight of the adventure.

Lord, Guard and Guide the Men Who Fly

Lord, guard and guide the men who fly
  Through the great spaces of the sky;
Be with them traversing the air
  In darkening storms or sunshine fair.

Aloft in solitudes of space,
  Uphold them with thy saving grace.
O God, protect the men who fly
  Through lonely ways beneath the sky.

Our congregation at Seabrook Methodist Church sings this prayer-hymn on every Sunday morning that one of our astronaut members or friends is in space flight.

Imagine if you can the depth of my feelings as I stand before my congregation when one of our own is orbiting the earth or on his way to the moon. What can I say that will speak to the emotions of my listeners—especially to the son of a deceased astronaut who might have been on this particular mission had he lived. What can I say to the scientists, the many technicians and professional people who have staked their experience and knowledge on the fact that everything was ready to go.

It seems to me that it is in moments like this that God's redemptive power is felt in an unusual way. He gives the words that are appropriate and satisfying, and He gives us the urge and the will to pray.

Praying together as a congregation for one of our own in space at that very moment is a moving experience. The words used may not be theologically correct or cohesive, but God "looks on the heart"—He knows what we mean and He understands our commitment. It is possible that the many reporters present may not be able to interpret the mood of the congregation, but to each of our members this bond of prayer fellowship is intensely real.

In all of our moments of worship—singing, praying, preaching—it is not so much what we say, but how we say it—what we feel. This is the stuff of which life is made.

The Space-Walker

Astronaut Ed White captured the imagination of the entire world the day he stepped out of the security of his spacecraft and became our first man to "take a stroll" in space. It was an exhilarating experience for everyone who listened to Ed's words as they came in over the radio or who saw the pictures taken from the craft.

When the tragic Apollo fire snuffed out Ed's life, the world was shocked and saddened. People everywhere had identified with him in achievement. Now they mourned his death.

But Ed White was a man of vision—he had dreams. Dreams not for a long life necessarily. Length of days did not enter his thinking. What mattered most was what he was doing. He felt a part of an undertaking that was essentially spiritual. To go on in space exploration was to nourish the very spirit of mankind; to turn back was to perish. To him, perishing did not mean the loss of physical life, but the squelching of man's spirit.

He had dreams beyond his own finite existence. While I cannot properly express or interpret his dreams, there is one who can come closer to doing this than anyone else. Indeed, she was a part of Ed's very being.

Pat White quotes Ed's words: "This program is bigger than

124

Astronaut Edward White, America's first space walker. Gemini 4.

any one person." And then she continues, "He felt that lives would be lost, but that the conquest of space was worth the risk. He was concerned that if there were a tragedy, the space program might experience delay. He felt that the American people should be made aware of these risks and be prepared if lives were lost. Ed felt that the program was so vital for our country and our youth that it must go on at all costs.

"If this program were not continued, I feel that Ed's loss of life was a meaningless sacrifice. It is a great fulfillment for me to see the program continuing stronger and better than it was before the accident.

"This program is better and stronger; people in the program are stronger. We've come through the biggest tragedy that NASA has experienced, and now we are going to the moon and beyond.

"It was a tremendous price to pay, but if it took that to mature this program, then some good has come from it. Ed would be proud of the American people."

Pat concludes her comments, "My faith is stronger today. I believe God can take every situation and bring good out of it."

These stirring words come from one who has sacrificed much. Her dedication to the opportunities of the space age should challenge all of us to rise and meet the demands of the times.

Shortly before the accident, Ed White said to Pat, "If I should ever be remembered, I'd like it to be for helping the youth of our country." It was this spirit that has since triggered an exciting project—the Edward H. White II Memorial Youth Center. This is not merely a Seabrook or NASA community effort. It reflects the spirit of the nation, and contributions to the $300,000 building project are coming in from all corners of our country.

The Edward H. White II Memorial Youth Center will be built on a location adjacent to the church where Ed worshiped, Seabrook Methodist Church. It will house a Quiet Room where items of spiritual significance belonging to our Christian astronauts who have rocketed into space and fame will be placed. The memorial will also help tourists who stop by to see "The Astronaut's Church" to be caught up in the spirit of not one Christian astronaut, but many. The general public is very aware of the space accomplishments of these men, but here they will have the opportunity to know something of the men themselves.

The financial contributors to this memorial are thankful people. They are thankful for bold men of faith who lead us into new adventures of discovery. One of the pledges came from a young GI who writes from a military training school in Virginia. It is in the form of a New Year's resolution (1969).

Dear Secretary:

You will soon be receiving checks from me once a month as donations to the fund I understand was established as a memorial to Astronaut White.

As a matter of interest—and possibly of some amusement to you: (a) My basic check will be a tenth of my current salary. Right now that is $13.00; (b) Any amount above this will represent a penny per swear word or (gratuitous) obsenity. (This is a mild habit contracted only since I've been in the army, so don't expect too many pennies there.)

Sincerely,

Tribute must be given here to three women who are devoting so much of themselves to this youth center project. Pat White sees it as a living memorial to Ed through its influence in the lives of young people. And Trudy Cooper and Faye Stafford, wives of Astronauts Cooper and Stafford, write letters of thanks to every contributor to the fund.

When Ed White stepped into space, a world of people were with him. The Edward H. White Memorial Youth Center Building Fund is living proof of their continued identity with him. It will stand as a symbol of Ed's accomplishments and as a symbol of the many lives he has inspired.

And Problems Too

Every community has its problems, and the NASA area is no exception. The intense pressures that accompany space exploration produce shaky and taut nerves—which, in turn, result in a varied assortment of social problems.

A three-year-resident here is called an old-timer. Ask where he is from, and he may say, "I'm from Miami, Los Angeles, New York, Wichita, or 'Podunck'." This transiency hardly makes for stability. Geographic uncertainty spills over into the soul of the person and results in insecurity.

Nearly everyone involved with NASA feels the pressures of the space program. There are deadlines on the one hand and the push for perfection on the other, resulting in inner tension—and sometimes alcoholism.

On the other hand there are those who feel inferior, or *are* inferior! Alcohol changes their personality just enough to give them the self-image of success. The result for awhile is a self-confident projection—and then alcoholism.

Much of this sickness results from the commonly spoken untruth, "Everybody does it." A large percentage of those who try "it" discover they cannot stop. And ultimately they are dropped from the rolls of our so-called "responsible" society. When I read this last sentence to one of my parishoners who is a "dry" alcoholic, he added, "Either they drop out or they die!"

Admittedly many of us are not doing much to stop this social sickness. But the creative people in Alcoholics Anonymous are doing a great deal. They don't have all the answers. On the contrary, they are people who have problems. And that is the uniqueness of the group—they have problems and are willing to talk about them with each other. And in this sharing they find answers—answers that help check the spread of the disease. These people recognize that they in particular and society in general have a problem, and they are trying to do something about it.

This group is made up of engineers, lawyers, doctors, newsmen, authors, laborers, and construction workers. Approximately eighty percent are connected with the space industry in some capacity. Some go to church; others do not. But they are all dedicated to "the cure" of their own alcoholism and to helping others. AA members are involved in a redemptive ministry. There may be more "church" there than some of us can see.

It is a fact, however, that many of these people are working actively within the church. And from what I've seen, their witness has been a means of redemption for many. AA members on my church board help me in our common ministry to others. In a real sense they are co-pastors. When I see my own limitations in dealing with certain problem situations, I call on these dedicated people, and because of their understanding and concern, their influence cannot be matched. They understand, and it comes across loud and clear.

Modern Communications

Now we have a better idea of what the moon looks like. From an altitude of 60 miles we saw its surface, and from moon orbit we heard it described by eyes trained to recognize likely causes for its features. We saw and heard this taking place 232,000 miles away! That is quite a distance for men's voices to travel, and to most of us it seems too far to send a picture. But we received both clearly.

What kind of a communications systems can do this? It is made possible by the application of a discipline called Quality Control. Those charged with the application of that discipline —working within the limitations of money, time, and weight —deliver the best product possible. This procedure establishes the quality of the product, and it is this Quality Control that produces dependable communications systems.

For example, Quality Control gives us dependable live TV from space with a camera that can be held in one hand and weighs less than five pounds. Then to insure receiving clear pictures and understandable sound, a reliable supportive communications system must be installed on earth. And before the astronauts can send signals to us, we must be assured that they and the spacecraft are functioning properly. That in itself takes a bit of doing.

The major phase of ground support communications takes place in the Mission Control Center-Houston (MCC-H). This center provides centralized control of NASA manned space flight missions. It exercises full mission control from launch through recovery—including life systems, flight crew condition and activity, recovery support, and ground systems operations.

The Mission Operations Control Room (MOCR) is the principal command and decision area in the MCC-H. *Critical information* relating to spacecraft, launch vehicle and ground systems as well as aeromedical parameters from the worldwide stations, ships, and aircraft, is processed and displayed within the MOCR. Based on analysis of this continuous flow of information, personnel in this room must assess the spacecraft flight status and progress, and then, in time-critical periods determine the continuation, alternation, or termination of the space flight.

The primary positions and responsibilities in the MOCR are as follows:

1. Flight Operations Director: Responsible for successful completion of mission flight operations for all missions being supported.

2. Mission Director: Overall mission responsibility and control of flight test operations, which include launch preparation. In Project Mercury there were no alternative mission objectives that could be exercised other than early termination of the mission. The Apollo missions, however, offer many possible alternatives which have to be decided in real time.

3. Public Affairs Officer: Responsible for providing information on the mission status to the public.

4. Flight Director: Responsible for detailed control of the mission from lift-off until conclusion of the flight.

5. Assistant Flight Director: Responsible to the Flight Director for detailed control of the mission from lift-off through conclusion of the flight. He assumes the duties of the Flight Director during his absence.

6. Experiments and Flight Planning: Plans and monitors accomplishment of flight planning and scientific experiment

activities. The scientific activities have grown steadily as the manned space flight program has progressed.

7. Operations and Procedures Officer: Responsible to the Flight Director for the detailed implementation of the MCC /Ground Operational Support Systems mission control procedures.

8. Vehicle Systems Engineers: Monitor and evaluate the performance of all electrical, mechanical, and life support equipment aboard the spacecraft.

9. Flight Surgeon: Directs all operational medical activities concerned with the mission, including the status of the flight crew.

10. Spacecraft Communicator: Voice communications with the astronauts, exchanging information on the progress of the mission with them.

11. Flight Dynamics Officer: Monitors and evaluates the flight parameters required to achieve a successful orbital flight; gives "Go" or "Abort" recommendations to the Flight Director.

12. Retrofire Officer: Monitors impact prediction displays and is responsible for determination of retrofire times.

14. Booster Systems Engineer: Monitors propellant tank pressurization systems and advises the flight crew and/or Flight Director of systems abnormalities.

15. Guidance Officer: Detects Stage I and Stage II slowrate deviations and other programmed events, verifies proper performance of the Inertial Guidance System, commands onboard computation function and recommends action to the Flight Director.

16. Network Controller: Has detailed operations control of the Ground Operational Support System network.

17. Department of Defense Representative: Overall control of Department of Defense forces supporting the mission, including direction of the deployment of recovery forces, the operation of the recovery communications network, and the search, location and retrieval of the crew and spacecraft.

These computerized consoles keep ground controllers in Mission Control constantly informed about the spacecraft and crew's condition. When we hear and see the astronauts on

TV, you can be assured that in Mission Control all is well.

Superlatives are inadequate in describing Apollo spacecraft electronic communications systems. They are equal in every way to the Buck Rogers mode of travel now come of age. After you work through the following heavy details of the various spacecraft communications systems, you will get a glimpse of their complexity.

On board the Command, Service, and Lunar Modules is a telecommunication system which provides for the communication of voice, telemetry, and tracking and ranging data between the spacecraft and the manned space flight network spread around the earth, and between the lunar module and the man walking around on the moon. It also provides for spacecraft intercommunications and includes the central timing equipment for synchronization of other equipment and correlation of telemetry data. The telecommunication subsystem contains the following equipment:

a. Data equipment group
  • Signal conditioning equipment
  • Pulse code modulation/telemetry equipment
  • Up-data link equipment
  • Data storage equipment
  • Flight qualification recorder
  • Central timing equipment

b. Intercommunications equipment group
  • Audio center equipment
  • Headsets and connecting electrical umbilicals

c. Recovery force electronics equipment group
  • VHF/AM transmitter-receiver equipment
  • VHF recovery beacon equipment
  • Unified S-band power amplifier equipment
  • Premodulation processor equipment

d. Antenna equipment group
  • VHF/AM omni-antenna equipment
  • S-band high-gain antenna equipment
  • VHF recovery antenna equipment
  • Rendezvous radar antenna equipment
  • S-band omni antenna equipment

Controls and switches for operation of the telecommunication subsystem are located near the Lunar Module pilot's station in the crew compartment. Also, there are three separate groups of controls (one for each crew member) for individual control of audio inputs and outputs of the crew members' headsets.

Communications aboard the Lunar Module (LM) are divided into three subsystems, as listed:

- LM-earth subsystem
- LM-command module (CM) subsystem
- LM-crew member subsystem

The LM-earth subsystem provides telemetry, television, voice, handkey, and transponder communication to earth. Return from earth is in the form of voice and digital up-data. The LM-CM system provides voice communications between the orbiting command module and LM. Pulse code modulation telemetry data at 1.6 kilobits per second can be transmitted from the LM to the command module. The LM-crew member subsystem provides inter-communication for the LM crew, and voice suit telemetry communication is provided by the backpacks during lunar surface explorations.

The MOCR along with Staff Support Rooms (SSR), Recovery Control Room, Command and Telemetry System, Voice Communication System, and the worldwide network undoubtedly make up the most complex electronics communications systems in the world.

This has been a highly technical explanation of our sophisticated and complex communications system. It certainly emphasizes the fact that we have reached unbelievable heights in electronic communications. But, unfortunately, we have fallen down in communicating with our neighbor. While we have learned to throw our voices to the moon and back, we have not learned how to look one another in the eye and communicate!

There have been times when we were deeply concerned by the inadequate communication between spacecraft and those on the ground, but actually those relatively few times of bad

134

communication between the flight and ground crews are minor in comparison to the day-to-day lapses of communication between persons involved in the regular routine of family and community life. The advanced Apollo spacecraft and ground communications systems on the one hand, and the obvious lack of some person-to-person communication on the other, spotlight one of the ironies of man's present predicament—his technology has gotten ahead of himself. Can he catch up? Will he catch up?

Can man catch up? I believe he can. Certainly he has a lot going for him. There is everything to gain in his struggle to establish communications with other people.

In talking about human communications, let's use the analogy of electronic communications systems and show that communications between persons can, generally speaking, work the same way. It takes two systems to communicate: a transmitter and a receiver. And each station, or person, must have those two systems and use them in order to communicate. That we have them is plain to see. We transmit by talking and receive by listening. But one of our most common problems in using these systems properly lies in the fact that we are more willing to transmit than receive.

Just because we are quiet during a conversation does not mean necessarily that we are receiving. We may be spending that quiet time in assimilating information to transmit as soon as we can get a word in edgewise! As someone has said, "A bore is one who keeps on talking after you think of something better to say!"

People who do not receive do not transmit the best quality. They may talk to each other, but they don't communicate. It's more like a bombardment.

We have concluded that man can communicate. But now comes the second question—will he? If he is not willing to communicate, there is no help. On the other hand, if a person is sensitive to the needs of others, he *will* be anxious to establish relationships based on giving and receiving.

To be *open* to others, we must be *open* to God in the same way that Jesus Christ was *open* to people. When we are

135

receptive to the Creator's spirit of Truth, we are *open* to others. In accepting them and in listening to their needs, we transmit not just words and deeds but ourselves.

When this happens, our inner communications systems have proved highly reliable. The quality is there, and it is our responsibility to maintain it and upgrade it by exercising control.

It is Christ's Quality Control that keeps us functioning at our best.

NASA Prayer Breakfast

Some of us aren't willing to admit it, but we really do not accept or know people equally. No two of us see another person in exactly the same way—similarly, yes, but not exactly.

After reflecting on this for a time, it seems possible that we are happier in our relationships by not seeing everyone else alike. Can you imagine being known by everyone for exactly what you are? It's enough to realize that God sees and knows us for what we actually are. But to have a whole world of people able to do this is an unbearable thought. And worse still—how would it be to be known by everybody for something we are not?

When you look at things this way, you become a bit more willing to be a human among humans—struggling for reconciliation with each other, but still human. Because of this fact of life, we do not come to know who people are so much as we know who they are *in relation to us* in given situations. And have you noticed? When situations change, "they" change.

In my many encounters at the Manned Spacecraft Center and in our church I have come to know many of NASA's key personnel fairly well. But the one contact with a very small fraction of this gigantic community of people that has meant the most to me has been the weekly Tuesday morning NASA prayer breakfast. Each week a few of the best in engineering, technology, and management come together for prayer and fellowship. At any moment during the day or night persons can call me and unload their pain, joy, and questions, but this is one place that I, as a minister, can unload on others. Around that table of sharing, we melt into one body and become ministers to each other, and, hopefully, to others during the days that follow.

No one has to show up; no records are kept; no requirements must be met to get in—there is nothing that holds this group together except the spontaneous fellowship felt by those in attendance and the reward of getting to know each other just a bit better.

While we meet in the same place each week, no two meetings are alike. Each week is a new and fresh experience as we come together in the spirit of Christ, which is love in the highest sense. And we change—hopefully for the good.

Because of that miracle of fellowship, I am getting to know even as I am being known. If I had not been convinced before, I am now—knowing others is never an objective, analytical process; it is something realized in the moment through an honest sharing of selves.

What happens to me in these weekly meetings at NASA is a spiritual spin-off that our government would never have dreamed possible. That dream belongs to God; the experience belongs to us.

PART IV

Truth Through Meditation

Your Flight
Why Go?
Rockets On Our Rears
She's a Big Baby Now
The Race
Little Green Men
Susej of Hterazan
Knowing the Truth
We Are Brothers
We Hope So
The Biggest Event
Bugs
Real Time
A Big God
The Truth Is
NASA

Your Flight

When a manned space flight is scheduled, most of us are glued to the television set. Unmanned flights fail to interest us because we cannot identify with a computer guidance system, but with a manned "system," we can. And we do—by watching every detail from countdown to lift-off to splash-down.

You might call this modern man's highest thrill of vicarious adventure. The office worker, the teacher, the taxi driver—yes, and the scientist, technician, and the engineer—cannot go to the moon, but many want to.

And in an imaginary sense we do go. We are right there with the astronaut in the space capsule. Our stomachs feel weak and our lips are dry. "Thirty and counting" seems an eternity. A successful lift-off gives us some relief; achieved orbit gives us more; but a safe landing makes it complete. "We" have gone through the adventure safely.

Manned space flight always does this for us. These gripping moments excite us every time. Like football games, auto races, air shows, each manned space flight brings us to our feet in excitement. If it were possible to remove men from football, autos, and airplanes and replace them with robots, the audience would be lost. No, computers alone will not do. A man must be a part of the integrated guidance system of the spacecraft in order for people in general to experience involvement.

Manned space flight has proved to be a means for modern man's fulfillment. There was a time when every man was a swashbuckling adventurer. It was essential for survival. He had to hunt down wild game for his meat; locate a cave for his home; swim rivers to find new hunting grounds. Now, he pushes a pencil in an office, draws pictures on a blackboard, and drives an automobile through traffic for some script that in turn buys freshly butchered meat wrapped in plastic at the supermarket. Our modern methods for getting meat are very tame.

Can we recapture the spirit of adventure that was once a crucial ingredient of our very existence? We can get this answer during the next Apollo launch. Through the miracle of television, we can share in the excitement of the lift-off— we can be a part of every phase of the flight.

This vicarious adventure makes for a more aggressive pencil pusher, or teacher. That is good, and God is involved in everything that is good. I'm not the originator of this truth. His Son is. It is He who says, "There is none good but one, that is, God" (Matthew 19:17).

He said it; I believe it. To me, this means that He is with us every time we experience fulfillment through our involvement with a manned launch. This is no rational argument. It is a truth. A truth that "turns you on" when you turn on your television set and "see and feel" another space flight adventure.

Why Go?

Why go to the moon? That has been the question of the last decade. When many ask it, they are looking for tangible results—for something that can be seen and felt. They want to see the same monetary rewards from space effort that they see from their labors. There is the notion that space probes ought to pay off in the same way. While this is not to be discounted, there are other meaningful results just as important as the economic factors. Perhaps one of the most important is creative effort. Without this we would not discover our particular talents. We would not know what we can do or what we can become. While the tangible rewards of work are significant, the spiritual rewards are of greater value.

And so it is with space travel to the moon, to Mars, and beyond. The average person is prone to prefer to see and touch. Indeed space technology has let him do these things. Your teflon skillet came from our efforts to go to the moon. And so have a thousand and one other items—heat resistant paint that is used on street curbs to warn of dangers while driving, electronic gadgets from radios to a paraplegic's wheel-chair that are controlled optically with sight switches. The tragic Apollo fire inspired the production of new asbestos materials which will save the lives of many fire fighters.

Open-heart surgery draws on space technology for its knowledge of pumps and electronic gadgets. But the real impact of these space spin-offs is yet to come. We are discovering more things than we can assimilate into various channels that will result in benefit for everyone.

While I recognize the tangible results of our space efforts, there are other reasons for going to the moon that are just as important, or more so. These spiritual answers operate on a deeper level than man's psychology. Though, I assure you, psychology is affected.

To put it simply: man is going to the moon and beyond because he can't restrain himself. He is created this way. "And God said, Let us make man in our image, after our likeness: and let them have dominion over the fish of the sea, and over the fowl of the air, and over the cattle, and over all the earth, and over every creeping thing that creepeth upon the earth" (Genesis 1:26). Only in recent years has man caught up with the birds! Space travel reveals dramatically one way that man exercises dominion over the fowl of the air. The writer of these words would be shocked to see just how true his statement is. For man has soared beyond the habitat of birds. And he is still going.

Man was created to dominate. He can't help himself. He has to go to the moon, and once he goes and sets up housekeeping, the profit motive will come on stronger. And in this way more people will share the rewards of the adventure. In the meantime, man will be conquering other worlds—simply because he has to.

What causes a person to climb the tallest mountain in the world? The desire to conquer.

What causes anybody to discover anything? To better understand what it is that he has dominion over. The adventure comes in seeking that understanding. While we cannot all accomplish these feats, we can share in the thrills of those who do. The television pictures from space of Astronauts Eisele, Cunningham, and Shirra did this for me. "Keep those cards and letters coming," their note read, and thousands did just that. This big response indicated a common involvement in that space triumph.

At the same moment these space pictures were coming to earth, I was flying in my Beechcraft Bonanza back to Houston from a meeting. Somewhere up there above me were these free-floating astronauts. It took little imagination on my part to identify with them. "Just a little bit higher and I'd be right there with them," I thought to myself. True, that "little bit" was a long, long, way. But it was no problem for my imagination. In a very real experiential sense, their dominion of space becomes ours.

While it is true that man was created to dominate, that is just part of the answer. He was created to dominate in a certain way—through Jesus Christ, who said, "I am the way, the truth, and life" (John 14:6). He remains for us the way of truth in life—the way of sharing our technology, the way of humility in our accomplishments rather than haughtiness, the way of sobriety in dealing with what could be a deadly game. Any other way alienates and destroys and turns our accomplishments into human failures.

Man must exercise his dominion over other creatures. He has no choice but to do this since he is made this way, but he can choose the method, the manner, or the spirit in which he dominates. When man chooses to carry out his domination in the spirit of Jesus Christ, he feels deeply a sense of destiny in his deeds. He acknowledges that a Higher Power has placed him there, and this subdues his ego in the moment of triumph. You might say this sense of a God-given destiny keeps man in his place—higher than all things on earth, yet a little lower than the angels and much lower than God!

Not everyone involved in our space effort shares this sense of destiny. There are agnostics and fatalists, and their technological and scientific accomplishments are just as significant as the Christian who works beside them. But, where *their* attitudes are negative, where *they* believe in unbelief, where *they* wrestle with natural laws of the universe, the person who feels divine destiny carries within him a positive drive.

145

He believes God and wrestles with God's natural laws in searching out and finding the way that God has chosen for him. With his antenna out, he receives signals; he receives a purpose for living and for doing his job.

Where is such a man? It isn't likely you'll find him shouting his righteousness from rooftops or in orbit. But his subtle actions reveal who he is. For instance, while many astronauts orbited the earth, they carried a Christian flag. Filled with Christian symbolism, some of the flags will finally rest in the reading room of the proposed Edward H. White II Memorial Youth Center. The point is: the fact that they have the flags with them at all says something about their sense of destiny.

Our Creator calls us together in dominion over other creatures and objects of nature. But we become lower than these other creatures without some inner spirit that holds us up to our responsibility over the lower forms of life. Man's spirit to dominate can cause him to go to the dogs, act fishy, or live a life "for the birds." This remains his greatest temptation and downfall if he gives in.

While our pinnacle of success gives us a view that's unmatched, it also provides the setting for a harder fall. The way to maintain that success rests in the way a man thinks. "Let him that thinketh he standeth take heed, lest he fall" (1 Corinthians 10:12). That's the way down. The way up, out, and forward to new horizons of human accomplishments comes through Jesus Christ. I've never heard of anyone who really tried it that failed. He may fall short, but Christ's way will not fail him.

Rockets On Our Rears

Years ago the citizens of a town in New England were considering the installation of street lamps. The opponents of the bond issue, which was the source of money for the installation, argued that "The Lord made the night to be dark." They were willing for people to stumble around in the dark because the Lord made it that way.

This logic has plagued man from his early beginnings. "If the Lord had meant for a man to build a fire, He would have built him with breath of fire."

"If the Lord had wanted man to ride fast across the rocky plains, He would have provided him with the leg and hoof of a horse."

"If the Lord had wanted man to roll across the ground, He would have put wheels on him."

"If the Lord had wanted men to fly, He would have put wings on their backs."

"If the Lord had wanted us to go to the moon, He would have put rockets on our rears!"

We haven't stopped to consider that this is precisely what God is doing. He made man as you see him, without built-in wheels, wings, or rockets. But *with* a mind, a desire, a curiosity, an adventuresome spirit, a will to set himself on top of these conveyances. This *will* is an integral part of man's makeup. In fact without it, man would fall apart at the seams.

It is because we feel very deeply that the Lord is with our men in space that we pray for them. Nobody has to tell us— we know we must pray. Yes, the Lord is in it.

She's a Big Baby Now

Rocketry was born March 16, 1926, at Auburn, Massachusetts, on the launch pad of Dr. Robert Hutchings Goddard. The first rocket was so small that it could be picked up with one hand, and its first flight lasted 2.5 seconds and reached a speed of 60 mph before it nosed down to earth 184 feet from lift-off.

In forty-three years our rockets have been developed to where they weigh thirteen times as much as the Statue Of Liberty and tower six stories higher.

Rocketry will continue to grow and mature each time a new one performs its mission. How much it will grow is up to us, spelled U.S. It staggers the imagination to ponder the strides of rocketry during the next forty-three years—if we don't fumble the ball.

No one can know today what the end results will be, and no one needs to know. We are not responsible for what people in 2001 will do. Those living then will be responsible for their own decisions. We cannot carry the ball for them, and while we don't know what the next generation will do, we know what we must do to remain a leader in space.

It is possible that the time will come when somebody is going to say, "Let's drop space exploration for awhile." And he will give a dozen "good" reasons for doing so. You never defeat a good effort by using "bad" reasons. If and when that time comes, rocketry will not reach its ultimate maturity; it will die.

And resurrection is a hard act for men to pull off. Accepting this fact can help each successive generation to act responsibly, and it will cause them to keep resuscitating the breath of life into man's newest and most exciting mode of travel—rocketry.

Dr. Goddard's baby has grown to be a big one, and it is still growing—if not in actual hardware, on the drawing board. And if not on the drawing board, then in the dreams of designers.

Dreamers see visions; others see them come to life. I've watched Saturn V take off for the moon while muttering breathlessly, "I never dreamed it could happen." *But someone did.* And right now someone somewhere sees a vision out of which growth and refinement must come. As long as this continues, rocketry may have moments when it gasps for life, but it will be here to stay.

The Race

A few people within the NASA community feel that the space race with Russia is an unworthy motive for our space travels. And I personally am impressed with their search for motives of deeper significance than a race with a competitor. There are humanitarian motives here that should be recognized. That concern is shown in NASA's Applications Division where earnest efforts are being made to get the technological discoveries into the hands of the people.

I agree that humanitarian motives should play the biggest role in any endeavor, but since this is not likely to fit into the universal pattern, we must be open to the lesser motives that help people get along with each other in the ambiguities of human involvement. One such motive that can be used for man's good is the spirit of competition.

Man has a natural drive to get ahead, to preserve himself, to get attention, to be someone unique. Like a young pine sapling, each man struggles and stretches to make a place in the sun. And he is going to find that place one way or another. One way to find and keep this place is through war; an alternative is in peaceful competition.

Peaceful competition has long been the motive for noble achievement. It is the spirit that has made our nation great.

Our schools compete in an aggressive sports program, and we cheer them on. Industry produces a quality product because of competitive factors. The competition is often stiff for the attention of the opposite sex.

And today, we are competing with Russia in the biggest race that man has ever known. Let's make the most of it—it can produce a better world. But, as with any competitive effort, we must be prepared for the possibility of losing.

When Russia's Sputnik went into orbit, we felt a deep sense of personal humiliation, but we were shaken out of our lethargy. What we first considered a disaster for our country turned out to be a great blessing. Everybody wanted to know why we were not first in space, and congress had to act.

So often we are reactionaries when we ought to be "actionaries."

It is quite natural that our NASA astronauts are anxious to be the first in moon landing and exploration, but we can well expect our Russian competitors to do something spectacular in the future, too. This in turn will spur us on to even greater efforts. Every major space triumph by one triggers congratulations by the other. It's better to run a race and see one win than fight a battle and see both lose.

Little Green Men

With radio transmitters scattered across the country, airplane navigation becomes a simple matter, but how do our astronauts navigate in space? It is difficult for us to imagine how this is done. According to our space scientists it was an extremely complex problem until a year ago. Then, one of the greatest scientific discoveries since atomic energy was made—the discovery of pulsars in our galaxy.

Pulsars are a complete mystery. All we know is that they are out there. *And are they there!* To date we have discovered that there are eleven of these mysterious transmitters of the heavens, estimated at distances comparable to several billion round trips to the moon. They are positioned at fixed points in the galaxy and transmit radio waves in bursts in which the spacing is constant to better than a millionth of a second and with an energy per burst equal to ten million Hiroshima-type atomic bombs. Dr. P. R. Bell's figures show that the whole electrical output of the world's power systems in 1968, about four trillion kilowatt hours, stored up annually for 100 years would equal the energy in one pulsar burst! And yet in size these beacons are likely to be only a few thousand miles in diameter.

Few time measuring devices are more constant than pulsars,

and since their positions are fixed, they are of enormous value as navigation beacons. Simple direction finders in spaceships can latch onto these signals and tell the navigator his position and speed so that he can travel to his desired destination.

Whenever we are confronted with a mystery, there is bound to be a great deal of speculation. Just what are these galactic transmitters? One idea that is considered seriously along with others is the LGM theory—Little Green Men!

I laughed at this theory—nervously. After all, what kind of natural heavenly phenomenon could explode with such an incomprehensible violence? If one of those transmitters should stop for an indefinite period of time and then start again, who repaired it? Scientists tell us that if we used three of these radio beacons as a means of finding a fix within the galaxy, we could go in any desired direction. This opens up a vast potential in space travel, but how would we feel "out there" if we should meet somebody coming toward us who is going to where we came from?

There is no end to the imagination-startling questions, but a person with spiritual faith is willing to ask any of them. After all, he has already wrestled with sickness, suffering, and death.

But faith is something that must be practiced whenever a new problem arrives. Faith does not make it easy to face a threat of the unknown; it just makes it possible. In the case of the pulsars we have a mystery on our hands that staggers the minds of our best scientists. But we can believe that in time we will understand what is going on out there. And if there are Little Green Men "out there"—"Faith, where are you?"

Susej of Hterazan

As our space exploration continues and manned landings are made on the moon, on Mars, or on Venus, someone is certain to ask the question—if there is life on these planets, has God revealed Himself there as we believe He has to us here through Jesus Christ? In other words, if there is life on other planets in our solar system, or in another solar system, is there a Christ there too?

At this point let me say that I believe God can do whatever He wants. If He has chosen to create life on other planets, life is there. It's just that simple. If that creature has a mind, a body of some sort, and a spiritual relationship with his Creator, there is the possibility he has had temptations similar to man's. If that creature has chosen to obey his Creator, he may still be lounging around in his "Garden of Eden." But if at some point he chose "to go it on his own," he sinned, and God had the same problem there that He did on earth. This would have made it necessary for God to reveal Himself to them as we believe He has to us through Jesus Christ. This is ᵤot to speculate that He must reveal Himself this way, since the means of reconciliation is always up to God.

God might have decided to reveal Himself through a "chosen people," through some form of direct revelation, or just

155

the way He did on earth through Jesus Christ. He might have decided to be born into those creatures, take on their "humanoidanity," and thus perfect reconciliation with them through a Christ as He did with Jesus Christ here. If God should choose to be born in the hinterlands of any planet in any galaxy in the life of one named Susej of Hterazan, that God-in-humanoid might be called Susej Christ.

Naturally, all of this has been speculation, but if we trust God in Jesus Christ, we must trust Him unequivocally as the God of the universe. To Jesus, God was Father of Heaven and Earth. Either we believe this or we do not. If we get shaky over the possibility of life elsewhere, it simply means that we do not trust the God of the universe—we trust a god of this earth only, and that is not the God of the Bible as attested by the creation stories of Genesis. A little god of this earth is merely a projection of our own fearful minds.

Now, let's look at this idea of Christ on other planets from another perspective. As we see it now, there are no humanoid life forms on the moon. But as our astronauts land on the moon, and one of them has personally experienced forgiveness of his sin against God, Christ *is* there in the life of that man. "Ye are Christ's; and Christ is God's," said Paul (I Corinthians 3:23).

With this thought in mind, let's let our imaginations drift on out in space to Mars. While science does not support the fact of humanoid life on Mars (there may be other forms of life), let's suppose there is. Consider the possibility that tribes of humanoids live on Mars and that they are in the same state of alienation from God that we are, but, up to now God has not given them any clear revelation of Himself. When an astronaut, forgiven of sin and reconciled to God and man, steps onto Mars, Christ is there in the heart of the man! "Ye are Christ's" on earth, on the moon, on Mars—anywhere! Could it be that our God of the universe plans to bring Himself to creatures of other planets through earthman's space ventures?

One of my close astronaut friends told me, "No matter which of our men land on the moon first, there's going to be

156

a Christian flag planted there." This means more than a mere colored cloth on the lunar surface. It symbolizes the fact that God is there, even as He is back "up" here on earth. Where a man is willing to profess Him and share Him with others, God is there, and "God is love"—on earth, on the moon, on Mars and beyond.

Knowing the Truth

One of the tragedies of our time is that many people are still looking for truth in a "universe" that existed for our ancestors who lived hundreds of years ago. They are not living in today's space age, at least in the sense that they are a part of it.

In 1888 the Congress of the United States pondered legislation that would provide funds for an expedition to outer Siberia for the purpose of locating the hole that the sun dropped into when it set in the evenings! *That was just eighty years ago!*

Then there are those who still see heaven as *up there somewhere* rather than as a state of being with God. This must be a hangover from the three-storied-universe idea with hell "down there," life here and now on the earth surface, and heaven "up there." This must have been the universe concept of the orbiting Russian cosmonaut when he said, "I don't see God up here." This doesn't say so much about God as it does about the cosmonaut's archaic ideas of God's universe.

Space science can help us understand so much about our universe, and as Christians, we should want to know because it belongs to God. I believe that our acceptance of Jesus Christ can help us in accepting the universe. Jesus said, "And ye shall know the truth, and the truth shall make you free" (John 8:32). Knowledge of truth can free us from the insecurity of sin to the security of God's spirit, from fear to love, from doubt to faith, from a narrow, biased view to a wider, more free concept of the universe. I am not suggesting that we can understand all the mysteries of our universe, but we can be open to everything that God wants to show us. He has given us the capabilities to think and discover, and to fail to use them could be an indication of our failure to trust God. Let us make use of the capacities He gave us—to think, to choose—to accept truth no matter where it is.

In accepting the truth of a universe where our earth and other planets move around the sun while moons orbit the planets—and all of this going on at the edge of a galaxy where there are millions of other suns with their planets and moons—we acknowledge God, for He's behind it all. And the realization of an unimaginably expansive universe will either send your brain spinning or it will snap your eyes open as you exclaim, "My God, what a God you are!"

Our universe reveals that He is a mighty "big" God. The Bible tells us about Him—His nature, His will, His way, His truth. The truth of the universe and the truth of Christ's presence in the soul are one Truth—God Himself. Through our universe we know about God; through Christ we know Him.

We Are Brothers

When Dr. P. R. Bell said that all forms of life are brothers, I wondered what he meant. After an evening of animated conversation with this noted scientist, I came to at least a limited understanding of what he was saying.

Dr. Bell points out that from the vast array of animal and plant life we see a genetically related substance called DNA (deoxyribonucleic acid). DNA differs in patterns in much the same way that letters arranged in different order can be made to spell an almost endless number of words. But DNA has only four parts instead of 26. The number of DNA combinations is endless. Dr. Bell described the possible number this way: "It would be a big fat number, so big that there's no fun in it."

One form of life—a butterfly may be 131313214121 . . . this goes on for 10,000 spaces! Another kind of life—silver sword plant that grows on bare lava may have its DNA substances lined up like 231312231242 and goes on for 10,000 spaces. Stretches of these combinations may be the same in a man and a fish and a dandelion, etc. This indicates that there is a DNA common to all kinds of earth life.

And now comes some eyeball popping possibilities from space travel. What if a DNA is found on Mars that doesn't

160

have the same four code letters common to earth life? We would then know that there has been a seeding of the universe completely different from ours. That discovery would be startling to say the least. But it would be equally as startling if this same earth DNA is found on Mars, indicating a common heritage for all life forms.

Undoubtedly, most of us would tend to be a bit opinionated at this point in demanding that it must be one way or the other. Many scientists fall into this trap. But the men I have talked with are not hanging themselves on the rope of some pet theory. They are open to the truth, whatever it is. That all life forms have to be one way or the other is not for us to decide. God has already made that decision. And our ultimate trip to Mars will be an excursion to see just what God has done there. God made it. He must be pleased to see that we care enough to go see what He has done.

We Hope So

The community of astronauts, engineers, technicians, and scientists at the Manned Spacecraft Center are the "hopeingest" group of people I have ever seen. That word "hope" is used within the environs of NASA as much as any place in the world.

If you talk to a biologist in the Lunar Receiving Laboratory —the place where any known life form from the lunar surface will ultimately be deposited—and ask him if the equipment there will keep any lunar "bug" from escaping to endanger earth animal or plant life, he will say, "I hope so." He will then attempt to explain the mysterious intracacies of the Lunar Receiving Laboratory.

When the Command Module returns from lunar orbit, it will carry the astronauts who have been on the lunar surface. Any microscopic "bugs" hitching a ride on them or on the lunar samples or on the boxes containing lunar samples will in turn contaminate the inside of the Command Module, including the command pilot who remained aboard while the others journeyed to the moon's surface in the Lunar Module. When the astronauts, their lunar samples, and any possible hitchhiking "bugs" return to earth, the heat friction built up in the craft's re-entry through earth atmosphere will burn off any outside microscopic rider. But the possibility that there might be even one such "bug" on the inside of the craft is the reason the entire Lunar Receiving Laboratory was built. It was constructed so that any lunar materials or life would be contained in isolation here on earth.

After splashdown the Command Module will be placed onboard the aircraft carrier, the astronauts then climb through a plastic tunnel into a portable moving van aboard the carrier and remain in isolation within the van. Through a sterilization process, the lunar samples will be packed for an expedited flight to the Lunar Receiving Laboratory. The van, along with its cargo of astronauts, is then transported to a large receiving room in the laboratory at NASA. Next, a plastic tunnel is attached to the building and the men will walk through it, leaving the module and entering the building. Now the plastic tunnel is sealed, returned to the van, and the door is closed and sealed. It is all "bug-proof." The astronauts are then free to enter the area where they will live for a period up to twenty-one days from the time they left the lunar surface.

Here they can visit with families, friends, and newsmen through plate glass windows and speak through microphones.

In addition to all of the other essential facilities for living, the area contains an emergency operating room. Some of the Houston's best doctors will be on call to perform any required major or minor surgery. The moment any outside doctors or nurses enter the laboratory, they are quarantined and must remain with the astronauts and other personnel until everyone is considered safe. That decision will be made on the basis of whether a moon "bug" has affected the health of those exposed.

Meanwhile, the lunar samples will have gone to other parts of the building where they are carefully analyzed just in case there is some form of lunar life hanging on. With these "bugs" secure, we are safe. And while a layman is doubtless overwhelmed by these preparations, the biologist's comment rings with universal truth—after we've done our best in anything, from building a bird house to building a spaceship, from putting both your cold bug and the lunar bug in quarantine, all we can finally say is, "I hope it works."

The interesting factor here is that hope is not a strictly scientific experience, but a religious one. This indicates that the religious experiences of hope and faith are part of all of life's experiences, including the scientific ones. And this quality of hope makes for better scientists. The top Manned Spacecraft scientists I know will put all of their brain power to work to do a good, stable piece of work, and they will hope and pray like the rest of us that all goes well.

The Biggest Event

Frequently, the journey to the moon has been compared to the sailing of Columbus to the New World. And there are some comparisons. Columbus prepared for six years to send three ships to this continent; America prepared ten years to put men on the moon. Columbus had money problems, and so do we. Columbus thrived on adventure—a spirit shared by our astronauts. Parties to both ventures were experts in navigation. There were some in Columbus' day who argued that the money could best be spent elsewhere, and "they" still live today. Sovereigns rose to greet Columbus and a seat was placed for him near the throne. Our spacemen are given a hero's welcome by all nations. And so the comparisons can be made.

But in a very real sense those comparisons vary so vastly in magnitude that they actually become contrasts. On his round trip Columbus sailed 9,000 miles on water—our astronauts are thrust over 500,000 miles into space by periodic bursts of fire power. Human life existed in the Americas, but there seems little possibility of it being on the moon. Columbus faced uncertainties within climatic elements familiar to him, such as winds, water, sea creatures—our astronauts face the uncertainties of elements foreign to them, such as micrometeorities, mico-organisms, vacuum, weightlessness. Columbus' boat was a means of transportation as old as man, but rockets, as fabulous as they are, can hardly be called "old." Columbus moved across the water but remained on the same planet—astronauts move out into space to a completely different planet.

Man on the moon is an event that surpasses all previous geographic discoveries. No scientific adventure has affected so many people. And with the aid of television and radio, the entire world is able to "be there"—to participate—to accompany the astronauts as they move about on the lunar surface.

And yet, this amazing scientific accomplishment that brings excitement to millions across the world cannot be compared to the greatest of all events in human history—the coming of God to man through Jesus Christ. I'll admit that my excitement during the Apollo launches tempts a comparison. But the contrast image comes into clear focus when I remind myself that where the combined copies of books of all authors on space will number a few thousand, the Bible has sold into the billions. It's the perennial best seller. The names of the space traveling, moon exploring astronauts will appear in all future history books, but their influence is relatively small as compared to the fact of God living in persons on this earth today. God born again in the flesh is the event to exceed all others—on earth, on the moon, and beyond.

Bugs

Space technology has revealed many truths, but none are more significant to me than the fact that there are "bugs" in the system. For example, the astronauts guided Apollo 7 to within five feet of the second stage of the rocket which is to house the Lunar Module on future flights and discovered that one of the petals had not opened up as far as expected.

Here are some of the other problems that developed: The 70 MM camera broke down, but was repaired by putting a little cream on the gears . . . the nozzles of some of the food bags clogged up . . . much of the food was too rich or too sweet . . . the drinking water was heavily chlorinated . . . at one point Donn Eisele told ground control, "Wally and I are trying to give away our butterscotch pudding, but no one wants it" . . . the nylon sleeping bags were uncomfortably warm . . . the extra sensitive circuit breakers shut down part of the spacecraft's electrical system for a few moments during the flight . . . a problem developed on the ground that didn't permit proper sleep cycles for the astronauts. But probably the biggest problem was the "cold bug" that plagued all three men.

Bugs, bugs, bugs! Why can't we have space missions without them? The reason is simple. The purpose of the early

Apollo missions has been to uncover the "bugs" before actual moon flight. The engineers and technicians try to imagine what they will be and correct them before they ever show up. But there must be flight tests in order to catch those that escape ground tests.

This preoccupation with looking for "bugs" in the hardware is one of the few occasions where looking for an evil becomes an acceptable approach toward a greater good.

And this is exactly what is being done in our search for safer space travel.

But under close scrutiny this statement does not mean what it seems to at first glance. We are not looking for bugs that we can kill; we are searching for those that can be changed into a positive part of a system that will keep our men safe up there. So in our preoccupation with an evil that, unless corrected, could cause tragedy, we are motivated by a good purpose. This means that our search for an evil is ultimately a search for good.

In saying this, let us not delude ourselves into thinking that witch-hunting has come to be acceptable in the space age. Looking for an evil in that sense is not in the least corrective. But it is quite fatal—to the project or person analyzed as well as to the witch-hunter.

It seems to me that the lesson to be learned from this thought is that it is important to know why we are looking for "bugs." If we do so because we enjoy looking for trouble or evil, watch out. This is dangerous. On the other hand, if our motive is to locate the ultimate good, our search can be creative.

In this latter sense we might be classified as participants with our Creator in His search for "bugs" that can be converted for ultimate good. In theology that is called redemption.

Real Time

When Astronaut Frank Borman, command pilot of Apollo 8, was asked what he would do if the Service Module's engine refused to start during lunar orbit, leaving the crew locked in the moon's gravitational field, he replied that he didn't know and wouldn't even think about it. That would be a decision that could only be made in "real time."

That phrase is an interesting one. What does it mean?

What philosophers might call a decision made in the existential situation, astronauts would call a "real time" decision. And the layman would call it an on-the-spur-of-the-moment decision, expressing it something like this: "I'll cross that bridge when I come to it."

No, astronauts don't know what they would do in such a "real time" situation. Neither do we know how we would react. We might say, "I will do thus and so." But in truth we don't really know now what we will do in the future. When that "real time" comes, we might react in a number of ways.

I'll dare to make a few educated guesses as to our reactions to a tragedy. True, these are guesses, but they are "educated" in the sense that they represent human reactions that have been observed in similar situations.

In any disaster there are those who will condemn the venture, whatever it is. In case of a space tragedy, some would be ready to scratch the whole program. A typical reaction might be: "We're monkeying around with something we have no business foolin' with." A thinker like this sees such tragedy as a supernatural displeasure of God.

And then there is always the witch hunt that follows accidents. Somebody must be assigned the blame—there must be a scapegoat. If there isn't any, find one!

These are simply ordinary human reactions to any unpleasant situation. In the case of a space tragedy, it would be much the same—and more. The list of reactions could be a long one.

We would like to think that not all reactions will be the negative kind. There are positive reactions to a negative situation. A glimpse at a tragedy may be a glimpse of hell itself. That is a terrifyingly negative situation. In that moment we might say, "Father, let this cup pass from me." Or, "My God, my God, why has thou forsaken me?" If we do call upon God in our moments of apparent aloneness, that is about as positive as we can be. At least we will have called upon *God!*

After listening to that first Christmas Eve worship service from lunar orbit, we can make a guess as to a possible reaction of that crew in a tragic situation. Since they included God in their highest moments of exciting adventure and pleasure, it would seem natural for them to call on Him in a despairing situation.

The key to making the best out of the worst comes from God. It is very likely we will call on God when the tragedy comes if we take Him seriously in the good times. But planning to include God in our lives tomorrow won't work because "tomorrow" never comes. Taking God seriously is a "real time" decision that must be considered in the present. Not yesterday, not tomorrow, but now. God's being with us always takes place in the now. It has to be this way, for God's nature is Being—itself, being the same yesterday, today, and forever.

A Big God

Space science gives us the ability to look at our earth in different ways. When you are walking across a green valley among wild flowers, it looks one way. Riding in an automobile along a freeway gives quite a different perspective. Airplane passengers enjoy a view that no landlubber could imagine. The views vary according to altitude. Flying is not the same at five thousand feet as it is above the cloud cover at thirty thousand feet—the impressions of the earth are as different as they can be. These impressions change even more from an orbiting spaceship.

From the vantage point of the moon the earth looks just like the moon except it is four times larger and eighty times brighter.

Earth viewed from Venus would look like the evening star (Venus). It would look more like a light than a mass of water and land. Where does that leave us in our concept of the earth? I think we will have to agree with Frank Borman that it isn't very big after all.

Taking this one step further, it also means that we humans are not as big as we think we are. On the other hand, look how "big" it makes God. If we could go *far* enough out into space, earth's light would disappear. But, if we continue on and on and on, the outer limits of space could still not be reached even though we would be approaching infinity. That's approaching God! Rather, I should say, "If this could be done, that's approaching God." But infinity is unapproachable from the human vantage point. This is true whether you search inside the universe of the atom or in our universe of moons, and planets, and suns, and galaxies.

Some scientists insist that the universe is expanding at a fantastic rate; others say it is shrinking just as fast. But even if it is shrinking, what is left is so expansive that the world's best computers cannot read a number to measure it. The best computer at the Manned Spacecraft Center can raise 10 to 1024, which is the equivalent of one followed by one thousand and twenty-four zeros. While there are no words to describe this number, the figure is not even a beginning to the answer as to the size of the universe.

This just begins to give us an understanding of infinity—of God. This same "unapproachable" God of the universe is the God of the Bible. The Bible does not show man finding God, but it does tell how God has revealed Himself to man.

Science shows the Creator is not limited to space. He is nonspatial, and that is precisely what the Bible reveals about God. He is in space, beyond space, but still right here.

This has been the witness of the Church for 2,000 years. God has shown us who He is in Jesus of Nazareth, and we are free and capable of putting His way to the test in this life. Everyone who has surrendered to His Way, attests to the fact that the experience of being found by God is real. The God of the universe and beyond meets us right here where we are.

Since we cannot approach Him, He approaches us, and says, "I am with you alway, even unto the end of the world" (Matthew 28:20).

The Truth Is

The Truth is: the space program has so many implications for good that I firmly believe we have not even begun to see all of the benefits that are possible in our Manned Spacecraft Program.

However, we must be sensitive to the possibility that some men in the future may be tempted to use the amazing discoveries of the last few years for evil purposes. The Creator has put in men the ability and desire to hunt and search and discover. To squelch that spirit would smother Truth and handicap God. It is Truth working in man that goads him to probe and find and learn. He just can't help himself, but he can "help" what he does with what is discovered.

This fact demands that we be alert. The discovery of the wheel resulted in enormous good, but it also produced a vehicle to crush and destroy an enemy. This has been true of every major discovery—it has been used for good and for evil.

We cannot afford a misuse of our lunar landing capability. And maybe, just maybe, man's occupation of the moon will lead him into the consciousness that war must be outlawed. Astronaut Frank Borman has expressed hopes that pictures of the earth from the moon will awaken people to see the necessity of peace on our good earth. From the moon our earth looks so small that it seems only possible for one family to live here. We are one human family, and families may have problems, but they must work together for peace.

It is true that most wars are fought for the purpose of survival, but that same urge can be utilized to stop wars. When we are genuinely overwhelmed with the fact that our very survival depends on not fighting, what is to keep us from using that urge for survival to stop wars? Nothing. Peace is possible. Space science can help mankind to face that fact. There is good here, but what happens with God's good creations, the earth, the moon, and other planets rests finally in the hands of man.

NASA

When Moses came down from Mt. Sinai with the Law of God translated on tablets for the Hebrews' direction, the people shouted, "Nasa V'nishma!" Translated into English this means: "We will do it; we will hearken."

In the first language of man (that we know about) through which God spoke divine direction, the people responded, "Nasa!—We will do it!"

Through the common vision of Jules Verne, H. G. Wells, Obertti, Tsiolkovsky and the great scientists of the past, Galileo, Kepler, Newton—the Creator of this vast universe has spoken, "This is your universe, explore it." This great human dream of the ages was given to the American people to act upon. And the American people said through her leaders, "Nasa!—"We will do it!" Space exploration is a national commitment.

It seems that divine destiny through a tiny orbiting Sputnik pushed us into the task of fulfilling truly universal visions. To most of us this commitment came from a source beyond ourselves. We were for it, but could not explain why. Only a few dared to speak out against these space missions. We seemed to be involved in something that somebody else controlled. Even our astronauts sound more like prophets than some of us who think we are. Again and again they refer to God's presence with them in their missions. Who is in charge here?

Is there an answer to this question in John 15:16?—"Ye have not chosen me, but I have chosen you, and ordained you, that ye should go and bring forth fruit, and that your fruit should remain . . ."

I wonder who named America's space agency "NASA" (National Aeronautics and Space Administration).

Was this President Eisenhower's idea? I wonder if Mr. Webb had a hand in its naming. Or could Mr. Goddard have muttered the words years ago only to have someone recall them later?

Is it possible that the Spirit of God in man named it? No, that isn't likely, but then I wonder. . . .

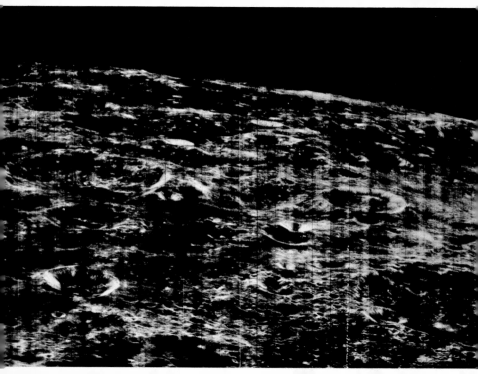